THROUGH THEIR EYES

THROUGH THEIR EYES

A STORY OF DOYLESTOWN HOSPITAL

BY ANNE BIGGS

WITH A FOREWORD BY JAMES A. MICHENER

TOWER HILL PRESS

Library of Congress Catalog Card Number: 98-071689

ISBN 0-941668-08-8

Published in the United States
by Tower Hill Press

Book design by Rob Larsen
Putnam Street Studio

Typography by SMS Typography

To order additional copies, call or write to:
Doylestown Hospital
Administration Office
595 W. State Street
Doylestown, PA 18901
Telephone: 215-345-2184

To the original Betty Anne
And to RLL, always

CONTENTS

My friend Herman Silverman has been kind enough to remind me that the Doylestown V.I.A. Hospital opened its doors to the public of Doylestown and its area nearly 75 years ago. Through the years, I have known the hospital intimately. I used to mow its lawn. I had my tonsils taken out in one of its rooms, supervised by Dr. Frank Swartzlander. I passed it on my way to school and was aware of the good things that were being accomplished inside its modest walls.

Later, I had a major heart attack in its rooms and the great cardiologist Paul Dudley White came down and took up quarters in the area so that he could treat an old friend.

One of the gentlest relationships between the hospital and me was through my saintly Aunt Hannah Pollock, who served the hospital for many years as its visiting nurse. Doctors in the area relied upon her to help them with the rural births of half the children born in that period.

I watched the hospital grow in size and quality until it was a major contribution to the community.

I have always felt that the V.I.A. committee of inspired women have made a remarkable contribution to our community. I hope that the 75th anniversary will continue to be as fruitful as the past years have been.

James A. Michener   1997

James A. Michener
Austin, Texas
16 August 1997

W hat are the defining moments in the life of an institution, and how does an institution grow beyond its walls to become part of the life and being of a community?

These questions were the focus of much discussion as we began planning the events that would mark our hospital's 75th anniversary. The vision for our year-long celebration was nurtured by Elizabeth Gavula, a dedicated nurse and administrator by training and our resident storyteller by avocation. Elizabeth's title—vice president, mission effectiveness—allows her to interpret and share the rich legacy of 14 spirited women who, in 1895, translated the needs of a growing village called Doylestown into actions that improved the quality of life for all. Now, more than a century later, the legacy of the V.I.A. continues to shine as the driving force in a vibrant, thriving hospital on the threshold of another century.

This book is not intended as a public relations piece, nor are the events of our 75th year meant only as celebration. Rather, this book and other anniversary events are integral parts of the ongoing and ever-challenging effort to renew our spirit as a collective group of caregivers and to rededicate ourselves with unfailing passion to the needs of others. We sought to capture the simple and compelling story of how Doylestown came to have a hospital and what our institution has meant to the greater Central Bucks community for 75 years. We chose Anne Biggs, a gifted local writer, and gave her the freedom to tell this story as she uncovered it through interviews and research. There may be oversights—a small book with an even smaller budget cannot possibly mention every worthy name or story. There may be inaccuracies—the memories of us all fade over time. But as I read this book from my vantage point among the present-day caregivers and support staff, I feel strongly that it does justice to the many heroic people who made and continue to make Doylestown Hospital a place that has healed the bodies, minds and spirits of this community. Through many generations—with compassion and fairness, with mercy and justice—we have followed our original vision. We hope this book serves as an ever-present reminder of the legacy of thousands of people whose heartfelt spirit of healing and consummate passion to give of themselves illuminated our past and will light our way in the years to come.

Richard A. Reif,
president and CEO

ACKNOWLEDGMENTS

This is a "people's history." Without the contributions of the many individuals who shared their memories and mementos, and the many others who gave valuable advice and assistance, this book would be incomplete. To them all, I extend my deepest gratitude.

A special thank you to the book committee, headed by Elizabeth Gavula: Amy Bird, Sue Gordon, Chris Murphy, Linda Plank and Marcy Wheeler. Thanks also to Rob Larsen, Mike Zoglio, Terry McNealy, Alice Lawler, Peggy Farley, Rich Reif, Jim Brownlow, Dr. Ed Knopf, Prue Suydam, Elsie White, Barbara Allspach, Marilyn Harrington, Jaromir Marik, Kay Marshall Marik, Elsie Taylor, Irma Satterthwaite, Julia Benge, Eva Brinker, Mary Brown, Claudia Cornell, Dee Cox, Hillborn Darlington, Mary Devan, Al Hertzler, Virginia Hess, Carol Jensen, Emma Krauter, Arlane Little, Gerry McGarity, Betty Murray, Doris Reith, Dorothy Scheingold, Mary Lou Stec, Betty Ann Tucker, Elizabeth Volare, Millie Waddington, Lois Whittaker, Mim Parsons, Clara Bahner, Martha Drapeau, Kathryn McIlraine, Catherine Mangin, Esther Benner Weber, Doris McKinstry, Kathy Robinson, Marcia Telthorster.

Also to Abbie Larsen Biggs, Betty Anne McLaughlin, Sandra Colina, Adele Paxson, Carolyn Bachman, Ginny Christman, Sally Dunn, Janet Linsenmaier, Alta Ennis, Martie Hotchkiss, Carolyn Taylor, Pat Berry, Ruth Boland, GeorgeAnne Galinski Hutchinson, Mary McCaw, Judy Melson, Ruth Schleicher, Carel Ann Taylor, Liz Westcott, Pat Bitzer, Jane Edgar, Claire Glascott, Ruth Toner, Pat Governale Lacey, Doris Jane Miller, Betty Nunemaker, Ginny Vandegrift, Pat Yaroschuk, Dr. Frank Boland, Dr. Sirus Zenouzi, Mehran Zenouzi, Dr. Charles Burmeister,

Dr. Donald Souilliard, Dr. John Gribb, Dr. Richard Vanderbeek, Dr. Cliff Laudenslager, Netta Mason Laudenslager, Peggy McGarvey, Dr. Joseph McGarvey Sr., Helene Bryan, Dr. Jack Bryan, Dr. Ahmed Mazaheri, Dr. Daniel Nesi, Dr. Carl Shetzley, Marion Shetzley, Dr. Tom Woodman, Louisa Whitten, Terry Rathgeber, Helen Robinson, Fritz Riley, David Riley, Dorothy Kibbe, Elizabeth Mae Crooke, Leonard Esmond Crooke, Elaine Ewbank, Catherine Try, Mary Schoeller, Helen Yost, Lance Schneider, Art Couillard, Aubert Bibolet, Bernie Jalbert, Peggy O'Neill, Ethel Northington.

And Betty Twining Smith, Ginia Kinney, Betty Simon, Martha Sine, Jean Goldman, Elaine Carroll, Lester Trauch, Marge Franklin, Larry Rubin, Emily West, Milt Rutherford, Jean Rutherford, Bob Oliver, Sue Rawes, Steve Rawes, Bud McKinstry, Jean Chubb, Pat Stover, Debbie Moneta, Peggy Dator, Bonnie MacGregor, Sheri Putnam, Bob Bauer, Patsy Clayton, Debbie Camiolo, Debbie Sclan, Debbie Renner, Burt Wohl, Don Nehoda, Joe Hellberg, Mark Pressman, Carolyn Montgomery, Anne Funk, Lyle Glassmyer, Lois Hamilton, Joan Parlee, Dr. Harriet Davis, Judy Green, Jack Bitzer, Lisa Bailey, Bert Proulx, Karen McCurdy, Dr. W. Stover Wiggins and Dr. Thomas Richie. To the many others who assisted me along the way, thank you.

Those who contributed stories and interviews but who do not find their input recorded here, please be aware that your words and tales *have* been assimilated and are part and parcel of the story related in these pages.

Anne Biggs

I n the space of more than 100 years, the manner of addressing people—especially women—has changed dramatically. I found an early V.I.A. note in my research acknowledging the advice of the organization's legal counsel that the women should always sign documents with first and last names, not "Mrs." and their husband's names!

Throughout the book, I have attempted to include given names, when I could find them, to augment the recorded courtesy titles and husbands' names; for more recent decades, I use the more familiar terms of the times. There is a raging inconsistency to this style, since it more nearly follows available data, personal preference and usage than a rigid format. If this confuses any readers, I apologize.

For me, Mrs. Richard Watson will always be "Mrs. Watson," Mrs. George W. Kerr will always be "Louisa B.," and Mrs. Matthew Suydam will forever be "Prue." I intend no disrespect—only affection and the deepest admiration.

AB

THROUGH THEIR EYES

*Turn-of-the-century lawyers'
offices on North Broad Street
later played a vital role in the
origins of the town's hospital.*

I n April 1895, Doylestown, Bucks County, sheds its winter-
weary look and blooms again. Warm weather brings neighbors outside to enjoy the sunshine, spring showers send them
back inside, and an occasional late snow flurry catches them off guard.
This has been the county seat since 1813, the geographical, cultural and
economic center of a substantial piece of real estate in southeastern
Pennsylvania. Doylestown is bustling in the April air, busy growing up
to face the fresh challenges of a new century.

The town's location, at the intersection of two old and important
highways that transect the county east to west and north to south, determined its value from its earliest years. In 1895, what Doylestown *doesn't*
have going for it is heavy industry; what it *does* have is everything else.
The Agricultural Works is probably the town's major source of "industry,"
and the courts and surrounding prosperous farms provide the backbone
of the area's economy. Doylestown's hotels, shops and services cater to
the needs generated by these professionals and farmers—and by the
citizens and their families who fill those needs. Over time, the residents
have developed a hard-working gentility that blends culture and learning
with service and practical skills.

New homes are going up on the old Taylor tract on Oakland
Avenue, which used to be called York Street. Dr. W.G. Benner, who
bought the Shaw-Taylor homestead, is building a stone addition there at
the corner of South Main and East Oakland to house his animal hospital.
On the outskirts of town along Pine Street sits the new jail, just 10 years
old. Locals still swap stories about the original 1812 courthouse and jail
and the Ship Tavern at Main and East State. The tavern was torn down

3

Down near the train station around 1907, a crowd of men, horses and wagons surrounds Clymer's General Store.

4

so the town could build the impressive Lenape Hall in '74; the other two fell to make way for the larger and more modern 1878 courthouse.

Rev. Silas Andrews' Classical and English School at Court and Broad Streets opened back in 1837; by the time Doylestown had "accepted the school law" in 1850, Andrews' once successful enterprise had deteriorated and was taken over for a public school. The building was later demolished and the site was used for the Doylestown Public School, built in 1889 during a surge of major construction in the borough. Meanwhile, other schools have risen and some have fallen, allowing the town to offer a range of private and parochial education in concert with the new public school system.

In many ways, Doylestown is little different from most of its neighbors. For example, in many instances medical care is limited to what the local pharmacist or doctor can provide, since the nearest hospital is hours away by horse and wagon along rough roads. Babies are routinely born at home, and too many of those who survive birth will not make it through the rounds of childhood illnesses and accidents. Contagion is controlled by quarantine, and often people cross in fear to the other side of the street when passing a house with the dreaded quarantine sign on the door. Popular lore and patent medicines continue to hold sway with those unexposed to new theories and practice, but the germ theory of disease is a decade old, Roentgen has discovered x-rays, and changes are on the horizon.

Public transportation has developed from stagecoach lines (the first traveled once a week between Easton and Philadelphia beginning in 1792) to railroads (the rails of the North Penn Railroad reached town in 1856); by the turn of the century Doylestonians can easily and comfortably travel the county and beyond. Street lights first lit the town with "rosin gas" in 1854, then with electricity beginning in 1892.

Bucks County Prison, now the James A. Michener Art Museum, was designed by well-known architect Addison Hutton and built in 1885 on Pine Street. FROM THE BOOK *VIEWS OF DOYLESTOWN PENNA.* BY THE CLAY STUDIO

Telegraph service began in 1846, making way for Bell Telephone of Pennsylvania to come to town in 1880.

In 1895, the desperate need for sanitation improvements for the borough's 3,000 inhabitants stands out against these modern conveniences. A disposal plant and sewer system for the town are nearly a decade in the future. Currently, a steam engine pumps the borough's water supply to a distribution basin adjacent to the cemetery, as it has since 1869. But problems are arising with the water's quality and quantity…and with inadequate garbage and trash collection…and with the dust that rises from unpaved streets to choke and sting the eyes of passersby….

Into a Friday in April comes a fresh burst of spring air—a hint of hope floating on the breeze. This evening, 14 ladies will set in motion a series of events and a legacy of volunteerism that will still be changing lives in profound ways long after they themselves are dust.

Health Concerns, 1897

May: Mrs. Henry O. Harris and Mrs. Richard Watson were delegates to the National Convention of the Woman's Health Protection Association in Philadelphia.

August: The V.I.A. discussed Dr. Edward Hart's report about the borough's water and his analysis of the samples, which were "decidedly unfavorable." The women drafted a petition to send to borough council, asking it to look into the matter.

—*from the V.I.A. Minutes*

This portrait is believed to be Mrs. Richard (Isabella T.) Watson.

Doylestown Public School was erected in 1889 on North Broad and West Court Streets.

"To promote the health and beauty of the town"

On April 26, 1895, 14 women of the community met in Mrs. Richard Watson's parlor. They discussed whether they should start a women's society to accomplish such tasks as getting trash picked up off the streets, eliminating garbage strewn in alleyways and planting vines and trees to beautify public areas. They also aimed to do *something* about the summertime dust that rose in whorls from the streets when traffic went by.

Two weeks passed while these women spoke to their friends and families and built interest in making changes within their community. On May 10, they gathered again, 30 strong. The needs, as they saw them, were as compelling as ever, motivating these capable women to tackle the problems of the town.

"After some general discussion…it was moved and carried that we form an association to promote the health and beauty of the town," reported the handwritten minutes for the charter meeting of the new Village Improvement Association (V.I.A.).

These were the days of disenfranchisement, though the rumblings of women's suffrage had by now reached well into Bucks County and the homes of the intelligent, cultured, forward-seeing women who had formed the V.I.A. The club members earnestly undertook its mission, drawing up a constitution and bylaws to govern how it would operate. The first officers included Mrs. Richard (Isabella T.) Watson, president; Mrs. Alfred (Mary) Paschall and Miss Mary L. DuBois, vice presidents; Miss Ellen D. Smith, secretary; and Mrs. Henry O. Harris, treasurer. Dues were set at 50 cents a year. The association met once a month in the beginning, with an annual meeting the first Tuesday in May and special meetings when deemed necessary. "The ladies," as they were called in affection and respect—and, occasionally, in derision— gathered monthly in the Library Room of the town's great community building, Lenape Hall.

For the next decade, the entire community was frequently made aware of the V.I.A.'s presence—and of the ladies' willingness to tackle tough problems that arose to threaten the "health and beauty" of Doylestown. The group was relentless in pursuit of its goals, serving as something of a burr under the saddle of the all-male borough council by urging it to tend to matters of health and safety within and around the town. When council failed to respond, the women— not a voting citizen among them—moved. The V.I.A. minutes relate, devoid of histrionics, efforts large and small undertaken by the association with what became its trademark thoroughness and an admirable disregard for the "impossible."

The Cost of Dust Control, 1896
Running sprinkler for the summer:
$117.99 receipts for services
$81.85 disbursements
Mr. Buckman runs the sprinkler for 35 cents an hour.
—from the V.I.A. Minutes

In the words of Mary Scarborough Paxson, author of the history for the V.I.A.'s Golden Anniversary Pageant in 1945, "one wonders whether there were any masculine red faces when the frail, weak sex started this men's work." And completed it so well.

The street sprinkler project provides an example of an early success that gave the V.I.A. a taste of its power to buck the town fathers (including, quite possibly, their own husbands) and garner the backing of the citizens. When borough council refused to take responsibility for the state of the streets during the dry seasons, the ladies investigated options and costs, then gave the choices before them due consideration. By soliciting subscriptions of 40 cents each for the V.I.A. sprinkler to regularly lay the dust in front of homes or businesses, the new club raised funds to order the horse-drawn contraption and built interest in its good works. The V.I.A. then raised some dust of its own when it went head-to-head with the borough council on the subject of the availability of water. Although the sprinkler arrived in the summer of 1896, the water supply continued to be an issue for many years. The V.I.A. sought the best deals to run, maintain and store the sprinkler over the winter months, made a small profit, and replaced this "watering can on wheels" when it gave out. After 18 years, borough council finally bowed to the V.I.A.'s greater wisdom and voted to relieve the club of its tasks for keeping the dust down. The ever-frugal V.I.A. then rented the sprinkler first to the borough for 75 cents a month and later to the state highway department for a dollar a day. All this without "the vote."

Hospital Fund established

The V.I.A.'s tenth anniversary seemed to renew the members' interest in the work of the organization—as though the ladies had passed a test of time and could move forward

Spitting Dropped from Club's Agenda
Right from the start, the V.I.A. took action against the common practice of emptying the cuspidors from the *Intelligencer* building and the courthouse into the streets. Later, the club attempted to control spitting at the post office and in other public places. When repeated appeals did not bring results, the ladies eventually yielded to common sense: "The spitting committee reported that it did not appear to be practicable to secure the enactment and enforcement of an ordinance in the borough forbidding spitting on the sidewalk…the only way to correct the habit seemed to be to educate the people not to do it."
—*from the V.I.A. Minutes, 1903*

Read (and presumed written) by Mrs. Alfred (Mary) Paschall, V.I.A. member and past president, at the members' celebration, 1905

Ten years ago this tenth of May
a Girl was born named V.I.A.
The mothers all were much excited
And said "To be sure, we're quite delighted!"
Town fathers feared she'd prove a bother
And run the streets and make a pother.

There were thirty godmothers attended the christening,
And much talking there was, as well as listening
To words of wisdom and plans grave and gay
How to bring up this maid in the very best way.

A good constitution to her we must give
And by laws a-plenty we'll help her to live.
Three guardians she'll have as well as a scribe
To write down her antics to show to the tribe.
Her money we'll put in charge of a treasurer
Who must count all the pennies and be such a measurer
That she'll ne'er run in debt nor spend all her money,
For that, you all know, would be far from funny!

That all the townspeople might know V.I.A.,
A circular letter was sent out one day
Announcing her birth, and asking their aid
In making the town better fit for this maid.
Pick up the waste papers and keep the place clean,
Plant flowers and vines and soon 'twill be seen
That Doylestown's attractions will grow so apace
That all beauty lovers will flock to the place.

Though still quite an infant, V.I.A. was so neat
That she fussed at the papers that flew down the street.
So she made some blue boxes with V.I.A. lettered out
In clean white paint, and set them about
And begged all to throw their waste paper within,
Thus making the streets as bright as a pin.

Her next thought: How tiresome to have so much dust;
Cried, "Oh, for a sprinkler; have one, I must!"
But sprinklers cost money, and money was lacking,

So now she stirred 'round to get up some backing.
Kind friends out at Oakland came first to her aid
With an evening event at which money was made:
A fair, and a drill, and an afternoon tea
Added pennies, dimes, dollars, made money quite free.

But still more was needed, so now the maid said:
"If men can run papers, why, sure, I've the head
To get up a great daily and fill up the space
With big advertisements and news of the place."
She canvassed and coaxed, reported and wrote
Editorials grave, poems, essays of note.
The venture succeeded, the daily had paid,
And "hip, hip, hurrah," cried this brave little maid.

Now came the sprinkler, and, filled with delight,
V.I.A. ran it from morning till night.
Through trials and troubles, V.I.A. never shirks,
For years have passed by, but the sprinkler still works!

With a horse and a cart she starts out again
to tidy the streets and rebuke the slow men.
She cares for the Monument and thus does her share
To honor the memories clustering there.

To make the town shady and pleasant to view
V.I.A. planted trees, and they're growing well, too.
To help all the needy and make their lives bright
With sunshine and comfort has been her delight.

And now, lest you fear that V.I.A. is a drudge
And for that very reason should bear her a grudge,
Let me tell you, this maid is delighted to play
And frolic with glee on Reciprocity Day.
She can write, she can speak, she belongs to the Fed.
She goes to its meetings and holds up her head.
For a ten-year-old maid, V.I.A. has done well.
We're proud of her, love her,
V.I.A. and her Belle*.

*This probably honors then-president of the V.I.A.,
 Isabella T. Watson, who presided over the V.I.A.
 from its founding for three separate terms
 totaling 23 years.

The V.I.A. float for the town's
Old Home Week parade in 1912

with greater confidence in their abilities to choose issues and create change. Membership grew, as did participation in monthly meetings and the club's expanding list of activities.

Concern for a healthy community was at the core of many V.I.A. projects, from halting spitting in public places to improving the town's water quality. Inevitably, in November 1906 ideas began to surface for forming a hospital. According to charter member Katherine G. Ryan's *V.I.A. History 1895–1932,* "the need of a hospital in the town began to be discussed and the president, Mrs. Watson, asked that all members of the organization act as a committee to ascertain the sentiment of the

11

residents on this matter, and to see whether any particular plan could be advanced for the starting of such a project."

On January 21, 1907, V.I.A. members met with 22 local ministers and physicians and endorsed the concept of a hospital for Doylestown. The hospital fund they established named as trustees Mrs. Richard Watson, V.I.A. president; Frank B. Swartzlander, MD; and William R. Mercer. Swartzlander and Mercer clearly threw their full support behind the project from the start, and it didn't hurt the effort to have two such prominent and well-respected *men* overseeing the fund. The women of the V.I.A. knew how to pick their battles. Three days later, the V.I.A. appointed a committee to interview the remaining physicians and clergy of the town to gather support.

The hospital fund grew slowly, through means that amaze and amuse us nine decades later. A sampling, according to Mary Scarborough Paxson's history: in 1908, the fund balance was $62 after younger boys of the town held a minstrel show; the Misses Ruos gave a dance; and boarders from "Oakland," a local summer resort at the old Doylestown English and Classical Seminary, provided an entertainment.

But interest in the hospital project developed steadily. When Dr. Frank Swartzlander presented a resolution in December 1910 for establishing a hospital in Doylestown, local physicians endorsed it unanimously. By 1911, the V.I.A. reported the fund had risen to $90.17—penny by penny.

Planting more seeds

Meanwhile, the V.I.A. continually discovered more tasks calling for its attention, many of which underscored the need for greater availability of health care in the

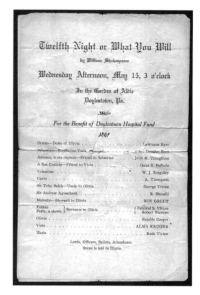

Playbill from a 1912 performance of Twelfth Night *held at Aldie, William and Martha Dana Mercer's estate, to benefit the hospital fund*
V.I.A. ARCHIVES

O.P. James Memorial
In 1997 the Central Bucks Ambulance and Rescue Unit corroborated that a substantial trust from the James estate continues to provide funds for purchase and upkeep of the ambulances. Letters painted on the side of several vehicles proclaim "O.P. James Memorial Ambulance."

The first O.P. James Memorial Ambulance,
a rebuilt Packard, and its driver

13

community. In February 1912, when a Dr. Murphy asked the V.I.A. for assistance, the club paid the fee for a nurse to care for a quarantined diphtheric child—opening the members' minds to the idea of providing a local nurse to serve the town.

When the V.I.A. paid to transport a Mr. Kline to Episcopal Hospital, Philadelphia, in Mr. Scheetz's auto delivery wagon in 1914, club members started thinking of other ways to better serve the town's health needs. In 1915, charter member Miss Sarah M. James and her sister, Mrs. George H. (Martha) Lorah, presented an ambulance to borough council in memory of their late father, Dr. Oliver P. James. On July 22, 1915, the O.P. James Memorial Ambulance delivered its first patient, John Mawson of West Court Street, to the newly opened Abington Memorial Hospital. The rebuilt Packard, equipped and maintained by the V.I.A., was replaced several times in coming years through the James and Lorah generosity.

But the ability to get patients in dire emergencies out of town and into distant hospitals did not fully satisfy the V.I.A. With the hospital fund growing so slowly, momentum now began to build for bringing a nurse into the community so the town could keep its ill or injured residents *within* the community. "The advisability and necessity of having a visiting nurse in Doylestown was discussed with interest, and the president asked each one to give it thought and see what could be done along this line," read the V.I.A. minutes for the September 7, 1915, meeting. The members discussed the matter further a month later: "This movement meets the approval of many." By January 1916, the idea took firm hold when the Charity Committee reported it had paid for a temporary nurse for yet another patient. The ladies made up their minds and appointed a committee, chaired by Miss Jane Watson, "to look into the advisability of carrying out this noble work."

Two months later, Miss Watson reported that she had called two meetings and had gathered information about different nurses and salaries. She advised that a Red Cross nurse would fill all requirements for a salary of approximately $75 a month. The question of how to pay for this—$1,000 annually—resulted in a generous anonymous offer of $500 toward the first year if the V.I.A. could raise the rest. The offer ignited the members' spirit and imagination, and ideas flew. With an objective in sight, the women were at their unflappable best.

Health care in Doylestown— before it was a place, it was people

Donations toward the Visiting Nurse fund were "coming in cheerfully," according to the Visiting Nurse Committee, and by June the women had reached their $500 goal. With the help of the Red Cross, a nurse was engaged to come to Doylestown. The town desperately needed the healthcare services she provided, though it did not yet realize how broad her role would become.

Miss Clementine Johnstone began her duties as Doylestown's visiting nurse on Monday, July 10, 1916, for $75 a month—about *43 cents an hour* had she worked only 40 hours a week—"and she keeps herself," the V.I.A. minutes noted.

It took no time at all for the V.I.A. and the town to wonder how they had gone so long without their own community nurse. When Miss Johnstone reported directly to the V.I.A. in August, the ladies discovered their first nurse was as direct as any of her women employers and as business-minded as any CEO 80 years later. She outlined how she intended to network with her physician colleagues, what strategies she'd developed for managing costs, her marketing plan and her community linkages. In her first three weeks she had made 62 visits and established

Unanimous Support

"Dr. Frances Janney Stoddart [of Riverton, NJ] gave a most interesting account of the work of the Red Cross nurse in that town… in the schools, homes and social service. Mrs. Henry A. [Miriam Watson] James made a motion that the committee should gather more information and report at the next meeting. Mrs. John P. [Harriet L.] Stilwell rose and said the committee had covered the ground thoroughly [and] made a motion that the Association might undertake the project. As this motion was in opposition to the previous one, [the president] asked a rising vote, which was unanimous."

—from the V.I.A. Minutes, March 7, 1916

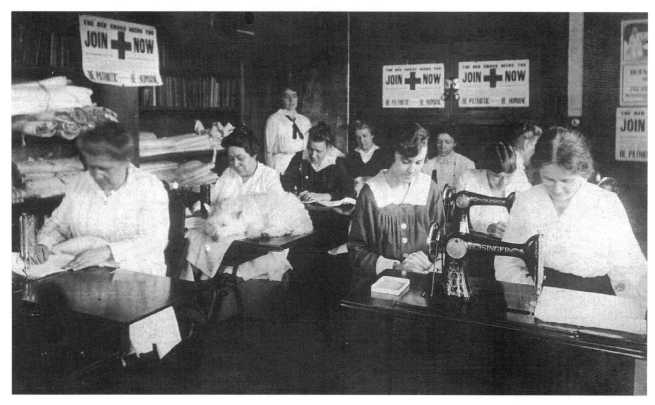

a rapport with local physicians and druggists. The doctors had offered encouragement and cooperation; she had been graciously permitted to place notices in the drugstore windows to advertise the nurse's services, fees and a convenient way to contact her.

The fees ranged between 10 and 50 cents a visit, to be paid to the nurse. Metropolitan Life Insurance Corporation policy holders received the services free of charge, with the company paying the V.I.A. directly for each visit.

By October, Miss Johnstone began to visit public and parochial schools and the community came to count on her. However, World War I intervened: on December 17 Doylestown's first visiting nurse left to join the Army Medical Corps and was replaced by Miss Eva Smythe.

Seamstresses with the Doylestown branch of the American Red Cross, founded in 1914, busy with their wartime sewing
COURTESY: MILTON RUTHERFORD COLLECTION

Miss Smythe, knowing that a healthy community begins with healthy children, requested a place in the public school building "where emergency equipment could be kept and pupils could be treated as the occasion demands," the Visiting Nurse Committee reported. It would serve, as well, as a permanent site from which to dispense health education.

But the war years made it difficult to keep nurses, and in August 1917 Miss Smythe departed for the Army Corps. For two months the town stumbled with a series of unsatisfactory or temporary nurses until finally in October Miss Norma Munsey came in, took over and stayed.

The townspeople saw Miss Munsey everywhere, pedaling her bike to visit patients and tossing penny candy—and informal healthcare education—to the children who gathered around her along the way. The kids loved her. She devoted herself to preventive health care, although the phrase hadn't yet become a part of the vocabulary.

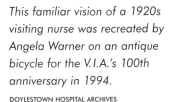

This familiar vision of a 1920s visiting nurse was recreated by Angela Warner on an antique bicycle for the V.I.A.'s 100th anniversary in 1994.

DOYLESTOWN HOSPITAL ARCHIVES

Meanwhile, the school district piped water into the nurse's room in the school and the V.I.A. provided a couch and pillow for $4.50. Within months of this "presence," services began to be added: in January, the V.I.A. made dental examinations and treatment available in the schools.

Epidemic

I n October 1918, Spanish influenza struck in epidemic proportions. The first local cases were reported in Perkasie on October 3; the next day Doylestown acknowledged 50 cases and the health department began to order closings. Although Doylestown wasn't hit as hard as other sections of the county, the town eventually reported 300 cases and just 7 deaths—compared to Perkasie's 961 patients and 23 deaths. Meanwhile, Philadelphia struggled with a daily death rate of 300 and, by one report, 3,381 new cases in one 24-hour period. If ever there were a time to be glad the city and its great hospitals were distant, this was it.

During the weeks of epidemic, Doylestown's local medical resources were stretched thin. Doctors and nurses fell ill themselves, further threatening the shortage of personnel. Red Cross volunteers filled in wherever they could. Miss Jane Watson, chair of the Visiting Nurse Committee, "spoke of efficient work during the epidemic…. It was necessary to employ another nurse for a short time."

Miss Munsey's arrival had coincided with the outbreak, and in her first report she told the V.I.A. of her record 741 visits for the month. The crisis cemented the community's trust in the V.I.A.'s Visiting Nurse Service and in the club's ability to make great things happen for the town. It also proved to the ladies the necessity of the healthcare benefits they were providing and strengthened their resolve to establish permanent emergency care facilities as soon as possible. At the November

Influenza
October 10, 1918: "The most important thought [sic] on our hands was the most efficient way to handle the new sickness, known as the 'flu,' in our community."
—*from Visiting Nurse Committee Minutes*

1918 meeting, with the last ripples of the epidemic and Miss Munsey's report still before them, the V.I.A. began making fresh plans. Mrs. William R. (Martha Dana) Mercer, president of the Doylestown branch of the American Red Cross and a V.I.A. member, offered the cooperation of the Red Cross in setting up a suite of rooms where the visiting nurse could bring patients who were unable to remain in their homes.

With customary diligence, Miss Watson headed a special committee that undertook the search for emergency rooms to rent. By March 1919, the committee had settled on two rooms it felt were suitable in a house on Broad Street, across from the courthouse and next to Bucks County Trust—just steps from the public school. The rooms were rented for $20 a month beginning April 1.

The Red Cross branch generously offered to equip and pay half the cost of maintaining the suite for one year. On May 13, 1919, the "splendidly equipped rooms" were formally presented to the V.I.A. Visiting Nurse Service. A week later, Miss Munsey and Dr. Frank Swartzlander held the first clinic, and Miss Munsey later reported "31 dressings and one small operation" at the site.

This forerunner of the Doylestown Emergency Hospital filled a need from the start: Miss Munsey reported to the V.I.A. that in June she and town doctors had treated 39 patients and conducted 15 operations in the emergency rooms.

"Splendid work"

As careful as the V.I.A. was regarding the quality of care it offered, it was equally diligent when it came to managing facilities and personnel. In July it authorized a joint "house committee" of six—three from the V.I.A. and three from the Red Cross—to manage the emergency rooms. A month later, the Joint House

Committee was sharing its efforts with those of the Visiting Nurse Committee on all aspects of both services. In the fall the Visiting Nurse Committee launched a drive to raise funds for the committee's expenses, and between October 14 and 16 it collected $1,854.50 and a pledge of $25 each month from the school board. A year later, a second drive netted $1,983.93—success enough to convince any doubters of the community's support.

The ladies also saw fit to give Miss Munsey's salary a boost to $100 a month in June—to all of 57 cents an hour!—and in September she took a badly needed vacation. Her worth to the town was obvious, and in January 1920, "owing to the high cost of living and in recognition of splendid work," the committee again raised her salary. Two months later, it bought her a car—a Ford Runabout—to make it easier for her to get around to her patients. In May, the V.I.A. heard the annual Visiting Nurse Service report of 3,360 visits for the year and expressed its gratitude and that of the community "for the faithfulness of our nurse, Miss Munsey."

Other appeals continued to draw the V.I.A. into adjunct activities that evolved later into functions of the hospital. For example, when the visiting nurse requested a layette for a needy family, the ladies established a sewing day that eventually became the hospital's standing Sewing Committee. For many years, these women met regularly to make and repair bed linens and curtains for the hospital. The V.I.A. also appointed a member to visit the rented emergency rooms each month, and until the early '90s the Visitation Committee routinely checked on the hospital and visited patients. No detail was too small to examine and pursue, if the women thought it had some merit and could forward their objectives to improve the health and beauty of the town.

In its minutes, the Visiting Nurse Committee documented its focus

No Flies on Us, Part I
One goal of the visiting nurse program was to eradicate the common housefly—or at least to make the public aware of its disease-carrying capability. Miss Munsey started a "Fly Crusade in the township schools, and would like prizes offered for the largest number of flies killed. Ten prizes would be sufficient, to present a prize to each school."
—*from Visiting Nurse Committee Minutes, April 1922*

Bucks County Branch, Southeastern Pennsylvania Chapter, American Red Cross

Martha Dana Mercer (Mrs. William R.), a V.I.A. member, was instrumental in forming the Doylestown branch of the Red Cross in 1914 to help relieve suffering during the war. A branch history, written by Erna Malen, reports that, in addition to equipping the rooms for the "district nurse," the Doylestown branch shared the cost of maintenance with the V.I.A. for the first year. The visiting nurse's emergency rooms were in the Randall building on North Broad Street, where the Red Cross also met for some of its work details.

The emergency rooms' original equipment totaled about $1,500 of branch money, plus individual and Red Cross auxiliaries' donations. Ms. Malen found this information: "The operating room had sufficient equipment to serve a hospital of 12 beds and the 'other room' was fitted up with two beds, one crib, and other necessary ward furniture including a cupboard with linens, blankets, medicines, etc." Also donated were a surgical table, sterilizer, instrument cabinet—and "four antique chairs and a tea set with tray." Items continued to arrive: water pitcher, desk and fittings, eye charts, asbestos brick, labor to make duplicate keys, electric lamp, stretcher and "reductions in goods purchased by different merchants." Later: eight-day wall clock, books and toys for young patients and a book rack for them, ambulance blanket, labor to vent the water heater to the flue, nursery refrigerator.

By 1920, the Red Cross responsibility for the emergency rooms had shifted toward an advisory capacity, with the V.I.A. taking on the full responsibility of operation and expense. As the years passed, however, the Red Cross continued to donate regularly and generously to the fund and to provide supplies. Around 1923, Mrs. John P. Stilwell of the V.I.A. requested that the Red Cross pay for a bed for the "Doylestown Emergency Hospital"—"the best type of hospital bed—raising and lowering devices with a nurse's cot underneath" for $60. If only a sketch had survived!

In 1924, the Red Cross provided a booth offering fruit, flowers and vegetables for sale at a "fête" for the emergency hospital. And from here on, the Red Cross contributed regularly, both money (averaging about $200 a year) and such hand-sewn supplies as "belly bands" and dressings—as time went on, less money and more sewing. As the work for the Chapter decreased, and the needs for the hospital increased, the workroom became, in effect, a hospital sewing room. "The same group of community-minded ladies were active in both organizations."

one year $1000.00 - $4.00 3 yr. $10.00 - 5 yr. $16.00
"   "   1500.00 - $6.00 " $15.00 - " $24.00
The Insurance was left in the hands of the
Pres. On motion it was decided to charge $5.00
for the use of the room in an operation and $1.50
a day while patient remains at the rooms.
Mrs. Mercer & Mrs. Atkinson was appointed
a House Com. for the Rooms for June & July.
Members present. Miss Watson. Mrs. Mercer.
Mrs. Swartley. Miss James. Mrs. Kerr. Mrs. Martin.

Minerva F. Martin
Sec.

June 30th 1919.
meeting of the Visiting nurse Com. on above date.
members present. Miss Watson. Mrs. Mercer.
Mrs. Swartley. Mrs. Kerr. Mrs. Atkinson. Mrs. Martin.
On motion it was unanimously decided to
raise Miss Munsey salary $15.00 making it
$100.00 a month to take effect at once, that
would be to start with June.
motion was made by Mrs. Martin & seconded

Snapshot

A visiting nurse lived in Margaret (Tommy) Tunnard's attic when Tommy was a little girl in the early '20s. She described the nurse's summer uniform as a white, long-waisted dress that belted below the hips. It buttoned down the front and had a Peter Pan collar and big patch pockets.

Tommy remembered that her family occasionally planned outings on Sunday afternoons just so the nurse could use the parlor to entertain a gentleman friend!
—from a conversation between Linda Plank and Mrs. Tunnard in 1997

on developing the nursing profession. In spring 1920, student nurses from Philadelphia accompanied Miss Munsey on her rounds as part of their training. A year later, the club wrote to legislators to support appropriation bills to assist medical education and employment for women, and the V.I.A. hosted a day-long gathering at the courthouse in May 1921 for the "nurses of Bucks County and their committees." That summer, the V.I.A. purchased a film on nursing education to support efforts to recruit women into this critical profession.

As the town's population grew and the age of mechanization gave rise to more serious accidents among farmers and industrial workers, Doylestown's dear Miss Munsey was gradually overworked. In addition to visiting patients in their homes, the visiting nurse taught hygiene at the high school, attended the well baby and dental clinics and worked in the emergency rooms. In August 1921 Miss Munsey was granted another raise, to $150 a month, and headed off for vacation. Miss Hannah Haddock, who had been engaged temporarily to assist her back in 1918 during the epidemic, took over once again and soon returned for good. That fall, the committee hired Miss Haddock as assistant nurse, her salary to be $90 a month during her three-month probation and increasing to $100 as soon as she was approved. The two nurses soon reported they were very busy in the emergency rooms, at bedside and in doing follow-up work with the community.

The Visiting Nurse Fund netted $1,582.55 during the October 1921 appeal. Donations of free services and the income from special events held by community organizations continued to come in to support the V.I.A.'s Visiting Nurse program and other V.I.A. activities. "Members were much pleased to know that other organizations were recognizing the value of the work of the V.I.A. and were wanting to help," the minutes related in November 1921.

In 1922 Doylestown's local newspaper, the *Intelligencer*, reported that the V.I.A.'s Well Baby Clinic celebrated its first year of operation with a baby show, noting that 1,500 children had been seen in its first 12 months. The minutes expressed special thanks to Mrs. H. Leroy (Marie James) Kister for her work with the clinic.

Another leap

The V.I.A., looking forward, at some point purchased five shares of "Building & Loan" stock, hoping to one day own a clubhouse. This step took the V.I.A. into the "risky world of finance," according to Katherine Ryan's history, and was viewed as a bold but chancy move in those times. However, it proved a wise venture when, in 1922, the John B. Livezey house near the center of town came up for sale. The trustees of the Hospital Fund bought the property at the corner of Pine Street and Oakland Avenue for $6,000 in May 1922 and leased it to the V.I.A. to use as an emergency hospital in place of the rooms on Broad Street.

Not until early February 1923 did the V.I.A. and Red Cross move into the new emergency hospital. Visiting nurse office hours were 1:30 to 2:30 every afternoon. A Mrs. Crouthamel was hired to take care of the premises, receiving "heat, light and lodging" in return for her general care of the hospital, its heater and telephone. Cutting a fine deal with the V.I.A. and Visiting Nurse Committee, she was paid "$6 a month for extra work."

The community generously supported this new and exciting venture of the V.I.A. Cash gifts of $1,500 came in for the nurses' salaries, and others provided medical equipment and household furnishings. To the V.I.A., having a hospital within the community meant its citizens wouldn't have to leave their home town to get quality health

Early Local Hospitals

1914   Abington Memorial Hospital, Abington, eastern Montgomery County

1916   Grand View Hospital, Sellersville, upper Bucks County

1922   Harriman Hospital (a private hospital), Bristol, lower Bucks County

1923   Doylestown Emergency Hospital, Doylestown, central Bucks County

1930   Quakertown Community Hospital (now St. Luke's Quakertown), Quakertown, upper Bucks County

1934   Elm Terrace Hospital (later North Penn), Lansdale, central Montgomery County

Frank B. Swartzlander, MD

care—and as an extension of that objective, the ladies insisted on making the new hospital as homelike as possible. Photographs from that period show rooms that are warm and inviting, furnished with curtains, lamps, dressers and comfortable chairs.

The V.I.A. incorporated in March 1923 to protect its members and its growing assets. On September 24, ownership of the hospital building was transferred from the Hospital Fund Trustees to the "Village Improvement Association *Incorporated*." The official "dedicatory" program for Doylestown Emergency Hospital was set for October 9, 1923.

T he work of this hospital and the V.I.A. can only be successful by united cooperation from the Doylestown public. I know that Doylestown will respond."

With these words, Mrs. William C. (Katherine G.) Ryan, president of the V.I.A., accepted the deed to Doylestown Emergency Hospital from hospital fund trustee William R. Mercer on Tuesday, October 9, 1923. The afternoon was a triumph for all those who had wished and worked this institution into existence.

"This is the consummation of a long effort," said Dr. Frank B. Swartzlander. "We have the equipment for an eight-bed hospital, if you people have the gumption to run it. There must be no internal friction and all must cooperate. Then we will see it grow and grow and keep on growing until it comes to fill a place in the community that it will not be possible to do without."

The new hospital had begun humbly, with a $3,000 mortgage to pay and daily expenses for nursing staff, patient care and upkeep of the facility. Inside the fine, three-story stone and frame house just a long block off Main Street was a reception room that welcomed visitors, staff and patients. A hallway curved around to the hospital office, new operating room and kitchen facilities. A receiving ward on the first floor held two beds. Upstairs, a bright front room with a bay window and a fully equipped middle room served as additional wards. The third floor had room for yet another ward. Meanwhile, a caretaker lived in the areas not used by the hospital.

Months before this official dedication, Mrs. John S. (Mary W.) Fretz, a recent widow, had come forward to establish an operating room in the

Doylestown, circa 1929

new hospital in memory of her husband. She contracted with well-known local architect A. Oscar Martin and his assistants, who donated design services for the handsome stone addition along the east side of the former residence. Once this was built, Mrs. Fretz conscientiously equipped it with "an adjustable operating table, sterilizing apparatus of the latest type, an instrument case enclosed in glass, basin stands, irrigator stands and special drop-light equipment for intensive illumination of night work." Six years later, the *Bucks County Medical Monthly* still referred to the John Stover Fretz Operating Room as "one of the finest…in Pennsylvania."

The Hon. William C. Ryan, husband of the V.I.A. president and himself president judge of the county courts, paid tribute to John Stover Fretz: "Some memorials are made of stone or bronze… some are works of art, but it seems to me if the retiring, unassuming gentleman in whose memory this wonderful gift is given could express an opinion, he must certainly have preferred to have his name associated and perpetuated with a place dedicated to deeds of mercy and acts of good will."

The dedication was an event the ladies of the V.I.A. and its Hospital Committee no doubt savored, despite having their "gumption" questioned.

Testing their gumption

All through its first decade, the hospital struggled to establish its reputation for medical, fiscal and community responsibility. As community healthcare and charity programs for the residents of the area expanded, many efforts overlapped into the realm of the hospital's interests and duties.

Into the new hospital came all the functions from the rented

Presidents of the Village Improvement Association

Mrs. William C. Ryan
(Katherine G.)
1922–1925

Mrs. George W. Kerr
(Louisa B.)
1925–1927

Mrs. Stace B. McEntee
1927–1930

Mrs. Calvin S. Boyer
(Mary R.)
1930–1933

Chairs of Visiting Nurse Committee, and then Visiting Nurse & Hospital Committee

Mrs. John P. Stilwell
(Harriet L.)
1921–1930

Mrs. George W. Kerr
(Louisa B.)
1930–1943

Mrs. John Stover Fretz
Lester Trauch, former reporter for the *Intelligencer,* can still picture the woman who gave the hospital its first operating room in memory of her husband: "She always wore a veil, and would ride in the back of a big car driven by a liveried chauffeur."

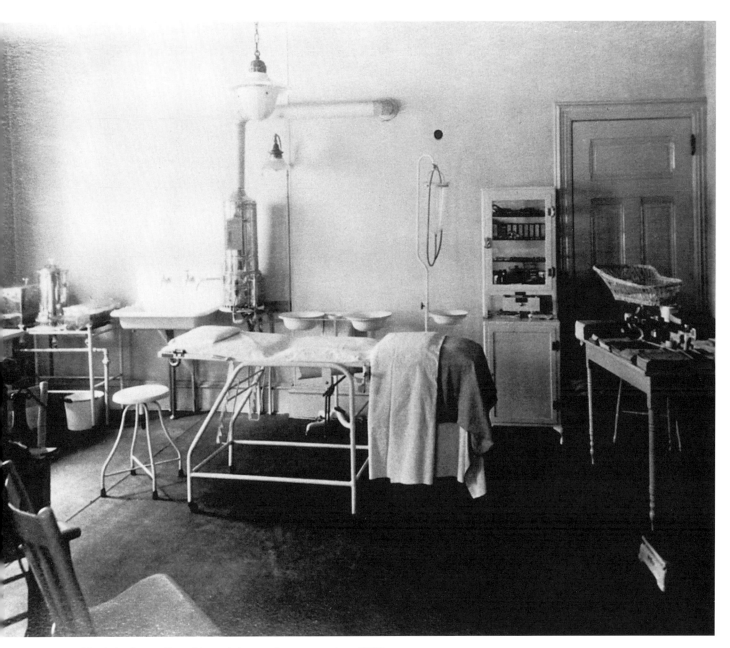

The John Stover Fretz Memorial operating room, circa 1923

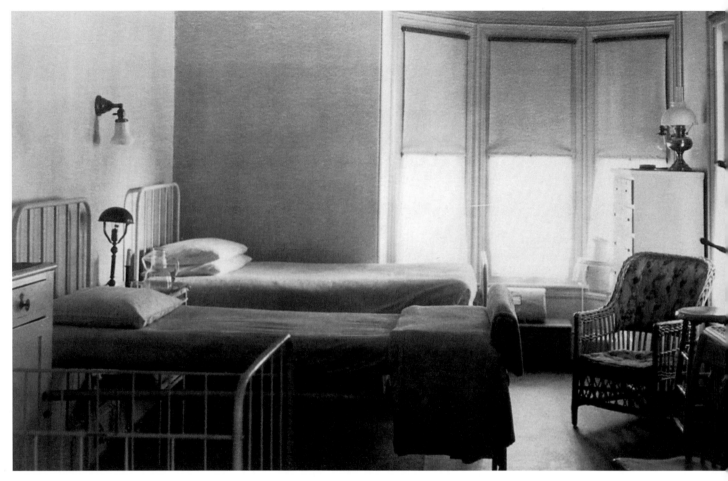

Second floor front room of Doylestown Emergency Hospital at Pine and Oakland, circa 1923   DOYLESTOWN HOSPITAL ARCHIVES

emergency quarters: community nursing program, child welfare clinic, in-house maternity and emergency services. The V.I.A. accepted responsibility for the institution and these integrated yet separate healthcare activities. The "Joint House Committee" evolved into the "Visiting Nurse & Hospital Committee"—or just "Hospital Committee"—of the V.I.A., with V.I.A. members serving as officers and on subcommittees.

These volunteers oversaw and assisted in the work of both hospital and community health programs. Generations later, the community

Cost of Health Care, 1923
"Use of Operating Room and
ether - $10 including nurses.
Maternity cases, including board
and nurse - $2.50 per day.
Delivery - $5.00. Board for any
patient - $2.50 per day."
—from *Visiting Nurse & Hospital
Committee Minutes*

is amazed by the level of commitment the hospital drew on in these early years to accomplish its goals. The minutes are replete with instances of committee efforts: women sewing shrouds because regular patient gowns are "much too short," providing special extras such as individual tea pots or a bedside lamp to make a stay in the hospital more pleasant, personally purchasing supplies and equipment they then donated, and drafting husbands, family and friends to make repairs or provide services *gratis*. Such gracious behavior through the years became the standard in this V.I.A.-owned and -operated hospital.

Turnovers in staff kept the Visiting Nurse & Hospital Committee busy. In October 1923, after six years as the town's beloved nurse, Miss Munsey resigned to marry Robert Leatherman and Miss Haddock became sole community nurse. A few months later, Miss Irene McAchren was hired to assist Miss Haddock, and Mrs. Grace Harrington was mentioned in the committee minutes as "resident nurse" at the hospital. Miss Mary Hutchinson came on as the first nursing assistant for the hospital in May 1924, for $15 a week.

With the average number of operations increasing from one a month in 1923 to five a month the next May, the hospital proved it was filling a need.

A new Willys-Knight ambulance was presented to borough council through the continuing largess of Miss Sarah James and the Rev. George Lorah; the V.I.A., which apparently made decisions regarding its operation, moved in March 1924 that "there will be no charge for use of ambulance for conveying person to or from hospital in the borough or nearby community."

In August the Visiting Nurse & Hospital Committee bought its first anesthesia machine, "it being the earnest request of Dr. F.B. Swartzlander." The committee usually took the advice of the doctors on requests like this, gratefully accepting their wisdom on matters of medical needs.

When September's hospital account balance reached $2,496.53, the V.I.A. agreed to pay off $500 of the mortgage with a gift from Miss Fanny Chapman. In October the V.I.A. and its committees geared up for the annual nurses' fund drive, newly labeled "Fund for Nurses and Hospital." But even as the V.I.A. women canvassed the communities served by the hospital for funds to support its programs, the hospital committees were making plans to pass along the charity. Among hospital statistics for December 1924 is this note regarding the visiting nurse program: "18 families were supplied at Christmas."

Upheavals occurred in staff again: Miss Haddock left to marry and was replaced by Miss Helen W. Lukens. In January 1925, a V.I.A. committee traveled to Philadelphia to recruit nurses. Soon the community and hospital nursing staff grew from three to five. A month later, the committee insured all the nurses in the Phoenix Indemnity Company. The borough school hired a nurse of its own, although the visiting nurse continued to run programs there.

A fitting tribute

T he hospital and the community reeled when news hit town in the summer of 1925 that beloved local physician Frank Swartzlander had died suddenly in London, closely following the death of his physician brother, Joseph, in the spring. By fall, the Doylestown Rotary Club established a fund to expand the hospital in memory of Frank and Joe, both members of the Rotary.

The new addition to the hospital was dedicated January 19, 1927. According to a local newspaper account, J. Carroll Molloy, Doylestown realtor and president of the Rotary, stressed that every dollar

Getting the Work Done, 1923
Early Hospital Committee sub-committees included a pantry shelf committee (canning and jelly-making), sewing committee (making and mending linens) and grounds committee (weed-pulling, bulb planting, getting the yard mowed and hedge trimmed).

Statistics on the Hospital
"Admitted 13 patients, 7 of whom were treated and dismissed within short time. One dieing [sic] when admitted; 5 remained for varying periods of 11 days; 1 died; 2 remained at hospital. Fees received from hospital during month - $161.25."
—first detailed hospital patient statistics for May 1924, from V.I.A. Minutes

O.P. James Memorial ambulance, Doc Sweeney and a nurse
Inset photo: Doylestown Emergency Hospital, circa 1938

33

of the $2,800 the club raised for this gift was given "voluntarily, with no solicitations," testifying to the "admiration, appreciation and affectionate regard" these local doctors inspired. The stone addition, built atop the Fretz operating room, created a modern obstetrical department with up-to-date delivery room, adjoining private hospital room, new bath and a "diet kitchenette" with sterilizing room attached. Reconstruction of certain areas on the second floor had widened the hallway leading to the maternity department and had added a semi-private room—for a total of 14 beds.

While the addition was a fitting memorial from the community, what accompanied the construction expressed more deeply the dedication of area residents to the hospital and their recognition of its importance in their lives. Mrs. Stilwell, chair of the Hospital Committee, detailed "the splendid cooperation of the neighboring community organizations." Warrington community organizations had taken over every detail of one ward, the Chalfont Community Club was completely outfitting the kitchenette and the Order of the Eastern Star had furnished the private room. Other church and community organizations had donated money, services and items to equip and furnish the new facilities.

Meanwhile, Mrs. Frank Swartzlander had donated her late husband's x-ray equipment to the hospital for its use. Unfortunately, the committee discovered, "we do not have anyone in our midst capable to use same." So Mrs. Stilwell consulted with Dr. J. Donald Zulick at Abington Memorial Hospital to establish some means to let Abington have access to the machine. In time, Dr. Harvard Hicks became adept at manipulating the plates and dials, and with occasional repairs and new parts, Dr. Frank's machine served the hospital capably for another five years.

Frank B. Swartzlander, MD, and
Joseph R. Swartzlander, MD

Community work

The "visiting nurse work," as the committee's minutes frequently referred to it, and the child welfare clinics were almost inextricably interwoven with the hospital's functions— as well as its physical space. As early as fall 1925, an eastern Pennsylvania Red Cross nurse representative objected to community nurses working within the hospital. Her concerns were proven in February 1926: the clinics were forced to move to the school dental room temporarily when a maternity patient was diagnosed with scarlet fever.

However, not until May 1926, when the Hospital Committee rented a set of rooms on North Main Street, did the community nurses and baby clinics get a home of their own. Unfortunately, the new site had no toilet, which didn't seem important enough to be mentioned until Miss Sarah James suggested, more than a year later, that it would be a good

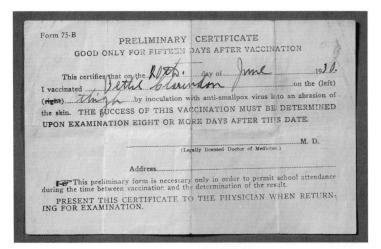

PRELIMINARY CERTIFICATE
GOOD ONLY FOR FIFTEEN DAYS AFTER VACCINATION

This certifies that on the 20th day of June 19 3 0.
I vaccinated *Betty Clarendon* on the (left)
(right) *thigh* by inoculation with anti-smallpox virus into an abrasion of
the skin. THE SUCCESS OF THIS VACCINATION MUST BE DETERMINED
UPON EXAMINATION EIGHT OR MORE DAYS AFTER THIS DATE.

.... M. D.
(Legally licensed Doctor of Medicine.)

Address..

☞ This preliminary form is necessary only in order to permit school attendance
during the time between vaccination and the determination of the result.
PRESENT THIS CERTIFICATE TO THE PHYSICIAN WHEN RETURN-
ING FOR EXAMINATION.

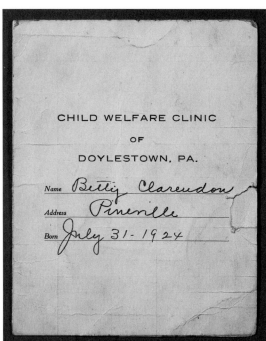

CHILD WELFARE CLINIC

OF

DOYLESTOWN, PA.

Name *Betty Clarendon*

Address *Pineville*

Born *July 31 - 1924*

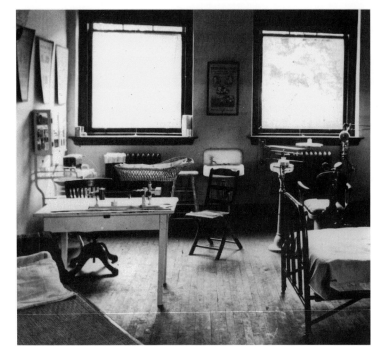

*This appears to be an early nursing clinic room,
with dental chair, sink, beds and baby scale.*

DOYLESTOWN HOSPITAL ARCHIVES

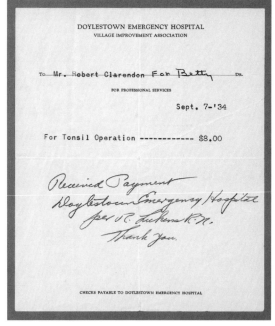

DOYLESTOWN EMERGENCY HOSPITAL
VILLAGE IMPROVEMENT ASSOCIATION

To Mr. Robert Clarendon For *Betty* Dr.

FOR PROFESSIONAL SERVICES

Sept. 7 - '34

For Tonsil Operation ------------- $8.00

*Received Payment
Doylestown Emergency Hospital
per R. Lukens R.N.
Thank You.*

CHECKS PAYABLE TO DOYLESTOWN EMERGENCY HOSPITAL

COURTESY: BETTY SIMON

V.I.A. Baby
Betty Clarendon Pearsall Simon, born July 31, 1924, in the Oakland Avenue hospital, was the first baby born there who went on to become a member of the V.I.A. (though not the first baby born at the hospital). She served as V.I.A. treasurer for seven years. Mrs. Simon was delivered by Dr. Sweeney, whose office was in the building on East State where photographer Charles "Lester" Maddox had his studio.

Baby Clinic Holiday Party
Twice a year, the Child Welfare Committee gave a party, complete with favors and refreshments, for all the clinic babies and their mothers. In December 1931, each of the 45 Christmas party guests received "a box of cold cream and handkerchief."

idea to have one. In February 1929, Mrs. Kister found two rooms—with a sink and toilet—owned by Lovinia Snyder Corson at 64 South Main Street, and this served ably as a health center for many years.

There, Mrs. Kister and later Mrs. Harris (Nora) Holmes chaired the Child Welfare Committee that worked with local doctors and the visiting nurses to immunize and measure babies and provide childcare education for their mothers. Clinics were held one day a week, with the Hospital Committee providing gifts and a special holiday party in December and a baby show with prizes in the summer. For some mothers, the clinics offered the only training available in diapering, feeding and bathing their infants. Dr. Herbert T. Crough administered the first tetanus anti-toxin injections there in February 1926, and was named exclusive doctor for the clinics in fall 1927, getting $3 for each afternoon session.

The Visiting Nurse Service labored unceasingly to meet the community's needs. In April 1926 Mrs. Emma Stover replaced Miss Myrtle Prescott as the visiting nurse assisting Miss Helen W. Lukens. When Miss Lukens resigned in the summer of 1927, Mrs. Hannah Haddock Pollock returned to her previous post—and didn't leave again until forced out by ill health in 1948. She became an institution in her own right, the "Miz Polly" remembered fondly by many of today's old-timers.

Mrs. Pollock helped bring health care and health education to borough school children—and later, to the children of surrounding townships' schools, establishing and capably staffing dental clinics, providing eyeglasses where needed, even teaching a "hygiene class" for highschoolers. In her "spare time," she distributed holiday baskets provided by the Hospital Committee to needy families, gave talks on aspects of health care when requested and maintained the hospital station at the Doylestown Fair.

Doctors and nurses

The emergency hospital, meanwhile, was kept busy dealing with the demands of space (or lack of it) and staff. In 1926 the committee began a project to enclose the rear porch for a new kitchen, which became part of the general Swartzlander memorial fund make-over. In August, the resignation of a nurse was demanded after reports were received of patient neglect. That fall, head nurse Miss Margaret Laubner regretted having to turn away a maternity patient because there were no rooms—a problem that renovations soon rectified. The January 1927 minutes used for the first time the terms "department" and "employee" to discuss the new maternity department and renewing employee compensation insurance. Ever mindful of its fiscal responsibility, the committee approved overtime visiting nurse pay for Mrs. Stover in October 1928 rather than raising her salary—then hired her two months later as supervising nurse of the hospital for $150 a month. Mrs. Reba Lukens was her assistant.

In spite of a new kitchen, problems were ongoing in the housekeeping arena. The committee negotiated often to get and retain help with cooking, cleaning and laundry duties. As soon as one month's minutes indicated a resolution, it seems the next month announced a resignation. A Mrs. Worman was on and off the staff several times during this period. Nurses and the committee members apparently were filling in when needed, since the only complaint the minutes refer to involved providing better food for patients paying a premium to stay in private rooms.

Early in 1926, the committee granted Dr. George T. Hayman, an osteopathic physician (DO), permission to use the hospital facilities for his tonsillectomy patients—he agreed to bring in a "full MD surgeon from the city" to perform the procedures—and for his conva-

Predictions

In 1926, Miss Ada Wood, field supervisor for the Southeastern Chapter of the American Red Cross, under whose auspices the Visiting Nurse program operated at V.I.A. expense, wrote to the V.I.A. She foresaw the day "when there will be no private duty nurses—it will be covered by Community Nurse Work. From the bedside work, the work grows, as not only the patient is treated but the family are educated at the same time. Bedside work should not interfere with educational work; they should work together."

A Penny Saved

Doylestown resident Betty Twining Kinney Smith is the daughter of Visiting Nurse & Hospital Committee treasurer Mary Twining. She remembers that her mother often sent her to pay the hospital bills in person to save the committee the cost of stamps. Betty would walk the few blocks up town to drop by local merchants' establishments and sometimes on to the hospital itself to deliver the nurses' pay.

What *Does* Happen?

Mrs. Pollock reported that she had spoken to three young girls who were described as being "wayward wanderers." She "warned [them] as to what would happen if they did not mend their ways."

—from *Visiting Nurse & Hospital Committee Minutes, October 1927*

Serving the Needy, 1928

"27 Xmas baskets were distributed by our nurses."

—from *Visiting Nurse & Hospital Committee Minutes*

Rat Tales

"Hospital Supplies [committee] gave a very good rat story at Hospital: with Mr. Hart's labor, his [the rat's!] path was blocked. Later a special food was prepared, and thus the end of the story."

—from *Visiting Nurse & Hospital Committee Minutes, August 1928*

Memories of Doylestown Hospital

by Mary M. Schoeller, Perkasie

Emergency Hospital at Pine Street and Oakland Avenue holds unforgettable memories for me. It was there, on January 26, 1931, that my first son was born.

At age 21 I was either the most innocent or the most ignorant female to have a baby, remembering only my mother's stern words, "It's the worst pain there is." In those days there was no prenatal training or birthing education such as exists today.

About 8 p.m. that evening, my husband took me to the Emergency Hospital. At 9 o'clock, my husband was told to go home. Other than nurse Doryliss and eventually Dr. John Sweeney, I was alone to face this ordeal. At 11:15 my son, Karl F. Schoeller Jr., was born.

This hospital bill for 11 days, at just $3.50 a day, was $38.50; delivery room was $5; circumcision, $3; 11 days of baby washing totaled $5.50. The bill from Dr. Sweeney, who was considered the best baby doctor in the area, was $40, which included monthly prenatal visits and two months of care after birth.

The V.I.A. operated a weekly clinic on South Main Street, which I attended regularly. I had no knowledge of how to care for a newborn, nor what to expect. He cried a great deal, which I thought was normal. It was only several months later, when he had failed to gain weight, that I was told he was starving and I must immediately bottle-feed him! For the next few weeks he gained a pound a week, and was soon a happy, healthy baby.

By the time my son John was born on June 23, 1934, the room rent had risen to $4 a day, with all other charges the same, and no charge for baby wash. Mrs. Emma Stover was the supervisor at that time.

I will always be grateful for the emergency hospital and clinic, both under the aegis of the V.I.A., and for the dedicated women who gave so much of themselves to their community. I congratulate them on reaching this milestone in their history.

lescing patients. This was not a popular decision among area MDs, but by treating new ideas and sincere effort with respect and fairness, the hospital built its reputation.

Doctors in the community used the hospital more and more, treating their maternity, minor surgery and emergency patients in the convenient, well-run facilities. The committee canvassed the local physicians in late 1927 to learn how they felt about community and hospital nurse work. It found that most of the doctors appreciated the services and were enthusiastic. Only one—a Dr. Rich—expressed outright disapproval of the hospital, offering as example that once a mother was brought the wrong baby to nurse.

Starting in November 1928, the committee extended free community nurse services to local physicians' and ministers' families—a courtesy that failed to survive into the 1990s.

Also in November, the V.I.A. Executive Committee appointed an advisory board for the hospital comprised of five men from the community: Fred F. Clymer, Frank Hart, J. Purdy Weiss, George H. Hotchkiss

Isabella and Jane Watson: Pioneers

Isabella T. Watson and her daughter Jane Watson must have been a formidable mother-daughter team. Both were part of the V.I.A. and the hospital from the beginning. It was in Mrs. Watson's parlor that 14 women met to discuss forming a women's organization to promote the health and beauty of the town in April 1895, and Mrs. Watson served as the first V.I.A. president and one of the three trustees of the original hospital fund.

While her mother led the club through its early successes on various community projects, Miss Watson researched and gathered support for the Visiting Nurse program. Through her efforts, the first visiting nurse was brought to Doylestown in 1916. Miss Watson died at the end of 1931; her mother, just months later.

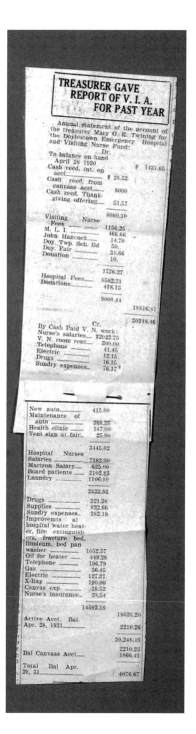

◄ V.I.A. reports of meetings, events, hospital and visiting nurse activities—and the hospital's financial statements—were regularly presented to the community in the Intelligencer, *the local newspaper. This treasurer's report is marked "1931" in Mrs. Kerr's hand.*

Behind the Wheel

A saga of unfortunate incidents developed around the automobiles used by the visiting nurses to travel their rounds. In those early years, the rural roads—and the nurses!—took their toll on the vehicles. In August 1929, Mrs. Charles H. (Cecelia B.) Shive of the Auto Committee reported that Miss Goldsmith, the substitute visiting nurse, "had been unfortunate, having had a few collisions, none serious." A year later the committee paid Hayman Radcliffe Motor Company $415 for a new Chevrolet with heavy-duty tires—having gotten $225 for the old car. The next summer, Mrs. Pollock's vacation substitute had a "mishap" with the Chevy. However, it was Miz Polly herself behind the wheel in June 1932 when this car met its end, almost taking Miz Polly with it. The accident was serious enough to keep her from work. Mrs. Stover, who had resigned in 1931 to work for the Tuberculosis Society, covered for her in the field. Mrs. Pollock returned to duty July 4, "driving the new car."

Wishes

In 1932, charter V.I.A. member Katherine G. Ryan's history of the V.I.A. closed with this vision for the future: "A large new Hospital, with the same type of efficient physicians and nurses as serve us now, two or three x-ray machines by means of which lurking germs may be located [?!], and a community, Hospital minded, who considers it a privilege to maintain it." While her understanding of medical technology may have some holes, her clarity of the V.I.A. vision cannot be faulted.

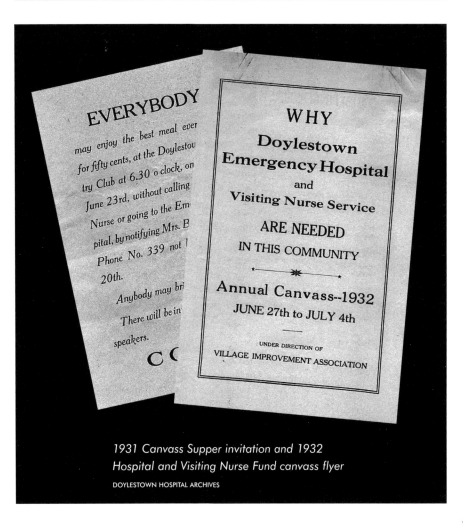

1931 Canvass Supper invitation and 1932 Hospital and Visiting Nurse Fund canvass flyer

and Nicholas F. Power. One wonders if the gentlemen were supporters of the V.I.A., admiring the members' intelligence and methods, or if they agreed to serve in order to "set the women straight" or to keep them from running the hospital into the ground. The hospital minutes of this period lack mention of advice asked for or received.

What drew nurses to work at Doylestown Emergency Hospital? The pay was unimpressive—and yet it became worse in mid-1932 when the Hospital Committee approved a 10-percent across-the-board pay *cut* after taking a look at a neighboring hospital's salary schedule. Vacations decreased from a generous month off with pay under original Red Cross Nurse standards, to three and then two weeks by mid-1930. When a nurse was disabled, as Mrs. Pollock was after an automobile accident, employee insurance covered medical bills and paid her about half her salary. Each Christmas the Hospital

What Difference Does a Decade Make?

On September 2, 1929, Louisa B. Kerr appointed members to these sub-committees of the Visiting Nurse & Hospital Committee of the V.I.A.:

For Visiting Nurse Work

☐ Child Welfare
☐ Township Schools
☐ Automobile

For Hospital

☐ House
☐ Grounds
☐ Linen

☐ X-Ray Machine
☐ Surgical and Medical Supplies
☐ Surgical Dressings
☐ Supervisors of Nurses

Plus Chairman, Treasurer, Recording Secretary, Corresponding Secretary

Ten years later, Mrs. Kerr appointed members to these sub-committees:

☐ Visiting Nurse
☐ Supervision of Nurses and Nursing Technique
☐ Medical and Surgical Supplies
☐ Hospital Bookkeeping and Budgeting
☐ Collection of Bills
☐ Social Service
☐ Supervision of House-cleaning
☐ House

☐ Private Rooms
☐ Kitchen and Laundry
☐ Linens
☐ X-Ray
☐ Laboratory
☐ Insurance
☐ Grounds
☐ Visiting

Plus Chairman, Treasurer, Recording Secretary, Corresponding Secretary

Nurses: Ruby Callahan, supervising nurse Emma P. Stover, Mrs. Reba Lukens (circa 1928–1931)

Committee authorized its treasurer to purchase a pair of silk stockings for each nurse, and sweet snippets of thanks appeared in the minutes in January. There was the chance to marry a doctor, as Miss Edna Baughman did: in October 1932 she said goodbye to her nursing supervisory post and became Mrs. Harvard R. Hicks and eventually the mother of three sons.

Maybe the appeal of the job was in touching neighbors' lives in a special way, helping them when they were vulnerable, even being close to the biggest events in life: birth and death. Doylestown Emergency Hospital in the '30s was hands-on, day-to-day, small enough to let each person feel that, nurse or doctor, paid scrubwoman or volunteer, she or he was a critical part of making life happen.

*Doylestown Borough's
centennial in 1938*

A s the population of the central Bucks County area grew, Doylestown became less and less isolated. Improved transportation and highways provided better links to both the town's rural outskirts and nearby suburban centers. The services offered by the Doylestown Emergency Hospital and the Visiting Nurse Service became increasingly important to the expanded community, and the hospital and community, in turn, attracted medical personnel to the area. The visiting nurse's reports indicated a steady increase in the number of doctors using her public health services, new doctors' names cropped up in the Hospital Committee minutes, and nursing and house-keeping staffs at the hospital continued to turn over.

The Hospital Committee demonstrated its own evolution as new members joined committees and added their unique personalities and skills to the mix. These two dozen women spread themselves across a variety of committees to oversee all aspects of running the hospital. The V.I.A. devised a technique that it continues to use today to identify its leaders: when a woman demonstrates interest, the club gives her critical tasks to develop her capabilities; how she handles various responsibilities reveals where her skills can best be used. In these early years, few V.I.A. women were trained to run a business other than their own homes, to balance books other than their own household accounts, to administer medical care for other than the sick or injured of their own families. And yet, they operated the fast-growing hospital and Visiting Nurse Service capably. When a member showed up with extensive experience or formal training, she assumed an obligation to use her skills to enhance the hospital and Visiting Nurse Service.

Aerial view of centennial parade in 1938

COURTESY: MILTON RUTHERFORD COLLECTION

Anniversary Celebration
Doylestown Borough celebrated its centennial May 29 through June 4, 1938, with parades, special events and a wood-bound commemorative book. The history of both the V.I.A. and its hospital—43 and 15 years old, respectively—is featured within.

Picture, for example, Mrs. Holmes. A registered nurse, she was busy with the practical work of the hospital, and her opinion on matters medical was sought often and confidently by the Hospital Committee. In the early '30s she chaired the Surgical Supplies Committee as well as the Child Welfare Clinic—where she was tireless in her efforts, if the committee minutes are any indication. Her "voice" was heard often, recommending the purchase of needed surgical items or describing plans for programs at the clinics. Educating the mothers was clearly one of her priorities. Her daughter Janet Linsenmaier recalls nurses coming to the house to talk over hospital matters, and Janet can picture the glass cabinets, filled with instruments, that lined the walls of a room at the hospital. Mrs. Holmes' other daughter,

Alta Ennis, later took up nursing. Both have been active in the V.I.A.

Although any woman over 18 has always been welcome to join the V.I.A., the club recognized in the '30s that some of the younger, community-minded women may have been put off by the perceived staidness of the V.I.A. In 1935 it formed the Junior Woman's Club to draw on the vitality of the *daughters,* 18 to 35, of the town. Until the Juniors disbanded in 1992 when the rise of professional careers and family responsibilities took their toll on the membership count, these young women made the pediatric department their special responsibility. Their legacy of dedication and hard work is recalled in warm memories of holiday house tours, the Village Fair and numerous smaller events and fund-raisers around the town.

Into the community

Although the Visiting Nurse Service was a function of the V.I.A. and a responsibility of the American Red Cross, nearly all decisions regarding it and its finances were made by the committee that ran the hospital. However, some of the visiting nurse responsibilities began to be assumed by other organizations: in fall 1933, obligation for the TAT (tetanus anti-toxin) campaign was transferred to the Bucks County Medical Association. The needs of the community shaped the Visiting Nurse Service, and as the community changed, so did the responsibilities of the visiting nurse.

Doylestown had about 6,000 residents in the borough and township in the mid-'30s; the Visiting Nurse Service and hospital probably served at least 15,000 more from those scattered across the wide area shared with Quakertown Community Hospital, Grand View Hospital in Sellersville, Elm Terrace Hospital (later North Penn) in Lansdale and Abington Memorial. In town, consolidated grade schools and the high school served the community, while education in the townships flourished in rural one-room schools where hardy women, trained at such institutions as the Kutztown Normal School, taught eight grades of mostly farmers' children. The school physicians and nurses—and Mrs. Pollock—conducted routine physical and dental exams at all the schools. Mrs. Pollock also transported students to eye exams and other necessary treatments, worked with the school nurses to bring health education programs to the elementary and high schools, and apparently provided basic dental care out of "the dental car," a vehicle given no further explanation in the Hospital Committee minutes.

The baby clinics, held one day a week at 64 South Main, brought in mothers and their infants for regular screenings, free of charge. In what was basically a well-baby service, the clinic doctor on call referred mothers back to their family doctors if he or she found problems. The nurse and the volunteers—Mrs. Holmes, other committee people, members of the new Junior Woman's Club—weighed and measured the babies, maintained records on each infant and answered questions or distributed literature relating to the perplexities of child care. Older children were offered pre-school physical examinations, tests and inoculation clinics among the other benefits.

The bulk of Mrs. Pollock's nursing care was delivered in the homes of the residents of this extended community. As valuable as the clinics, school and community work were, in many ways the heart of the Visiting Nurse Service resided in the warm, capable and efficient care she gave to those bound to their homes by childbirth or the infirmities of age, illness or accident. For those who received the ministrations of this sincere and tireless visiting nurse, her gentleness and warmth were no less critical to their well-being than her clinical efforts on their behalf.

Cost of Health Care, 1933
John Hancock and Metropolitan insurance companies raise reimbursement [for visiting nurse care] to 87 cents and 83 cents a visit, respectively.
—from Visiting Nurse & Hospital Committee Minutes, October 1933

Visiting Nurse Report for April 1933
305 visits to 59 patients for 10 doctors

Fees $76.55

17 patients' visits paid for by insurance company [at around 75 cents a visit]

206 children weighed in schools

one talk given at Parent-Teacher Assn. Meeting

21 children had dental defects corrected

4 sessions of Child Health clinics with 4 new and 167 return visits

one child training class with 40 in attendance

5 dental clinic sessions with 48 new and 7 return patients and 71 treatments

5 trips to hospital clinics with 3 new and 8 return patients

assisted in transferring 4 patients

336½ hours on duty

—from Visiting Nurse & Hospital Committee Minutes

The minutes of the V.I.A., the Visiting Nurse Committee and later the Hospital Committee make it clear that Doylestown's early hospital was never intended to replace or compete against services offered by larger, established facilities such as an Abington Memorial Hospital (opened in 1914) or the big city hospitals. The ladies' modest intention, which most of the residents stoutly supported, was to provide local services in "routine emergencies": accident and wound care, childbirth, tonsillectomies and other "simple" operations. Initially, the hospital at Pine and Oakland wasn't open around the clock, and until 1928 the minutes are sketchy regarding just who was in charge of the patients.

The availability of this emergency care surely saved lives and improved the quality of life for area residents. But while the hospital continued to expand in size and services, corresponding to the growth of the community, it appears to have maintained a view of itself as primarily an emergency facility, even to retaining the name Doylestown *Emergency* Hospital into the mid-'50s. When the complexity of a patient's case warranted, the decision was made quickly to transport him to Abington or into the city to the care of specialists and the more advanced equipment and elaborate facilities these hospitals could provide.

However, it is also true that before the hospital achieved accreditation, some doctors and local residents withheld consent for treatment at Doylestown Hospital even for routine care. Even after accreditation was awarded in 1955, the hospital struggled for another 20 years or more to alter its reputation among some people as essentially a local emergency facility, one that those who could afford quality care from the best professionals wouldn't consider for themselves or their patients. Not until the move to West State Street, coupled with the tremendous growth of the area, was Doylestown Hospital finally able to shed its "light-weight" reputation and fulfill a certain destiny—one much greater than that envisioned by its founders.

For her services—and she let the committee know this included about seven and a half hours each month preparing written reports—Mrs. Pollock received about $2,000 a year. The nurses' benefits included health insurance coverage and a paid vacation. A defroster was installed in the visiting nurse's car in November 1936, but she refused a heater. When the Hospital Committee decided in 1938 that maintaining a nurse's car was too costly, Mrs. Pollock agreed to use her own car, for which she was reimbursed five cents a mile. Small wonder the committee honored her contributions.

Changes in medical practice

Although Drs. Frank and Joe Swartzlander were gone, fresh names arose among the medical professionals in the town. Dr. Allen Moore, who succeeded to Dr. Joe Swartzlander's practice, was a popular man among the elite, according to local reports, and this put him in a position to wield power over the Hospital Committee—which he did. After all, many of the committee members were his patients, and they deferred to him readily. It wasn't the first time a doctor used his power, nor the last. For the most part, it appears his service to the community was sound and welcome.

Dr. Harvard R. Hicks—he who married nurse Edna Baughman—brought in a local boy, Dr. Redding H. "Fritz" Rufe, and the two were widely respected as deep scholars and top-notch diagnosticians. Dr. Hicks functioned as the hospital's x-ray specialist; later, he focused his attention in the field of psychiatry. Unfortunately, Dr. Hicks' open criticism of other physicians' techniques and manners made him unpopular with some in the medical community.

Dr. Rufe developed cardiology as his part-time specialty. A modest man, he was beloved by generations of patients and doctors alike.

Just Call Me…Version One
Dr. Harvard R. Hicks was nicknamed "Braxton" by his friends for British gynecologist John Braxton Hicks, who identified the "false labor" uterine contractions that carry *his* name.

Doctors Who Treated Patients in the Pine and Oakland Hospital

The last names of these doctors were found in the minutes and in a single, recently discovered hospital record book of 1934–38 non-maternity procedures. Because no formal "medical staff" existed at the time and information is sketchy, this list is necessarily incomplete and may contain inaccuracies.

Frank B. Swartzlander, MD
(1873–1925)

Joseph R. Swartzlander, MD
(1875–1925)

Robert L. Walter, MD
(1875–1956)

Herbert T. Crough, MD
(1879–1951)

Linford B. Roberts, MD
(1886–1965)

John J. Sweeney, MD
(1886–1944)

Allen H. Moore, MD
(1890–1971)

Gomer T. Williams, MD
(1892–1974)

Claude L. Taylor, MD
(1894–1937)

George M. Brewer, MD
(1895–1942)

Harvard R. Hicks, MD
(1897–1958)

George Thawley Hayman, DO
(1898–1984)

Redding H. "Fritz" Rufe, MD
(1901–1996)

Kenneth S. Scott, MD
(1902–?)

Edward E. Koonce, MD
(1903–1970)

Bradford Green, MD
(1903–1994)

David Kenneth Leiby, MD
(1903–1994)

Melrose Elmer Weed, MD
(1903–1932)

Paul M. Nase, MD
(1903–1993)

Thomas E. Lindsay, MD
(1904–1987)

William I. Westcott, MD
(1904–1989)

John W. Ward, MD
(1905–1959)

Ralph C. Farquhar Jr., DO
(1910–1980)

Frederick Lutz, probably DDS
(?–1987)

Paul O. Blake, MD

John F. Keithan, MD

Raymond B. Wallace, MD

Mathew Zahrzenski, MD

and Drs. Adams, Byer, Brown, Hague, Hamilton, Hankin, Hart, Hartman, Hawkins, Krauss, Matthews and Rich, about whom no definite information was found

Even the crustiest of physicians today have favorite Fritz Rufe stories to tell, and the admiration and affection are apparent in every word.

Dr. Bradford Green, one of Doylestown Emergency Hospital's most well-remembered physicians, came to town in 1935. Dr. Green's abiding interest was obstetrics and gynecology, and as a family doctor he built his practice baby by baby. Doylestown is populated with the fruits of his labors—multiple generations, too.

Two physicians whose names appear frequently in the earlier Hospital Committee minutes are Dr. John J. Sweeney, county coroner for many years and chief burgess of Doylestown, and Dr. Claude L. Taylor, who arrived in 1926. Doylestown lost these popular and respected pro-

Medical Practices of the Time

The Schick Test, administered by the V.I.A. at its Well Baby Clinics, was devised by Bela Schick, a U.S. pediatrician born in Hungary, to determine immunity to diphtheria. If an area of inflammation results after injecting dilute diphtheria toxin into the skin, the patient is not immune.

Ethel Northington, Nurse

Mrs. Northington, trained at the Army School of Nursing at Walter Reed Army Hospital, served Doylestown Emergency Hospital as a substitute nurse in the '30s.

"I remember the old hospital at the corner of Pine and Oakland—that was *the* hospital. And I'm telling you right now, no patients anywhere ever got better, more careful attention than the patients in that hospital. They practically got personal care.

"Any hour of the day or night, when they wanted somebody extra, my telephone would ring. I would hustle out of bed and waken my mother and tell her to look after my children while I went to look after somebody else's. I lived down on South Clinton Street…I'd walk up there at 2 o'clock in the morning and think nothing about it, but I wouldn't do it for a mint today. And I substituted an awful lot. I think I got $6 an hour when I was doing special duty, maybe $5 an hour for regular duty."

Although she was "just" a substitute nurse, Mrs. Northington was part of the close-knit hospital family. She remembers Hannah Pollock fondly—they were good friends. She describes "Betty Baughman," head nurse when Mrs. Northington first came to the hospital, as "an excellent administrator—quite young for that." Sophie Dietrich was a "marvelous cook—no hospital had a better cook." Emma Stover and Grace Bancroft were good nurses, good people and "a lot of fun," each able to tell great funny stories with a straight face.

—*from an interview conducted by Elizabeth Gavula in September 1994*

Early Anesthesia

Woodrow W. Try was a Dublin farmer by day and worked in a hosiery mill at night. One Saturday in 1936, as he bent over to fix the hand-cranked engine that chopped up silage, the engine backfired and blew off the crank—right into his mouth. Catherine, who later became his wife, found him, "blood all over." He had lost eight teeth and "that lip was just like a big piece of liver, hanging down," she recalls.

At the emergency hospital in Doylestown, he waited two hours for the doctor. Dr. Taylor had Try interlock his hands and put them behind his head. "That was all the anesthesia he had while the doctor stitched him up."

fessionals too soon. Dr. Sweeney died in 1944; Dr. Taylor was killed in 1937 at age 44 when the plane he was piloting crashed in Solebury.

Dr. Herbert T. Crough, who served as doctor to the Well Baby Clinic for several years, put in time as the school doctor in the 1940s. He and his family lived on North Broad Street in the former rented emergency rooms. There is little information available about Dr. Robert L. Walter, except that he supported the hospital, took his turn as physician to the Well Baby Clinic, and offered to exchange his stately Victorian residence for the Oakland Avenue hospital.

At this time, the hospital followed a system of monthly rotation for physicians on call. In 1934 Dr. Rich suggested an alternate plan, giving each physician charge of the service "to which he is most suited." This was the first stirring of specialization at Doylestown Emergency Hospital.

But such examples of forward thinking among the physicians contrasted with the difficulties osteopaths faced in this decade. The preserved documents of Hospital Committee chair Louisa B. Kerr include a letter to Dr. Moore in 1929 from the American Medical Association that warned the hospital against "cult practitioners." The association characteristically refused to register Doylestown Emergency Hospital until it made sure no osteopathic physicians were allowed to treat patients there. For some years, Dr. Hayman, residing in Doylestown and practicing here and in Philadelphia, had been approved to call in an MD-certified surgeon of his choice to perform tonsillectomies on his local patients at Doylestown Hospital. In mid-1936, the Hospital Committee voted that no other osteopathic physician but Dr. Hayman be admitted to the hospital staff.

Mrs. Kerr's correspondence yields a sampling of letters from late 1936 and early 1937 that shows clearly the renewed struggle within the hospital over the issue of allowing osteopaths to use the hospital—or limiting it to just the one. Dr. Hayman and Dr. Ralph C. Farquhar Jr. argued that their hospitalized patients had as much right to choose their physicians as any other patients. The Hospital Committee listened to Hayman and Farquhar—and to a growing protest organized by people of the community. In November 1936 it granted Dr. Farquhar leave to use the hospital for his maternity patients.

A letter in January 1937 proved the issue was still unresolved. Mrs. John C. (Agnes D.) Swartley of the Hospital Committee wrote that a Mr. Mays, superintendent at Abington Memorial Hospital, had assured her that "only those who have a medical degree either allopathic or homeopathic, and are members of their county medical society, can practice or attend patients in Abington or any other first-class hospital. Osteopaths, unless they also have a medical degree, are not allowed." Mays believed the V.I.A. was making a mistake by allowing osteopaths use of the hospital for confinements or any other procedures. Mrs. Kerr wrote Dr. Farquhar on January 11 with news that the committee had given permission for him to care for his patients in the hospital, but that his surgery was limited to circumcisions for the infants of his maternity cases. Two decades later, Dr. Farquhar voluntarily resigned from the hospital medical staff in order not to hinder the accreditation the hospital was then seeking.

Building anew

In the midst of dealing with a growing body of strong-minded physicians, new medical practices and technologies, rapidly expanding community populations and the continual battle to maintain the building and its nursing and housekeeping staffs, the Hospital Committee had to face the fact that the hospital had outgrown its quarters.

On October 14, 1934, 22-year-old Louisa Skoog and four relatives and friends were returning from her family's small farm in Dublin to her job with Merck in New York City. Her uncle was driving the new car—just about 600 miles on the odometer—south on Swamp Road when they were hit broadside at the intersection of Cold Spring Creamery Road by a truck from Philadelphia carrying tomatoes. The impact smashed Louisa, sitting on the left behind the driver, across the car and down onto the floor behind the front seat, legs over her head. All five passengers were treated at the Doylestown Emergency Hospital on Oakland Avenue. Louisa, the most seriously injured of their party, had fractured her pelvis in five places, and she would remain at the hospital under the loving care of Dr. Taylor and a host of capable nurses for eight weeks.

"I remember waking up in the hospital—the church across the street was covered with ivy, and it was loaded with birds singing and chirping."

Of her painful injury, she readily admits "at least three of the eight weeks were terrible." But she remembers the nurses and Dr. Taylor and Dr. Hicks fondly for the "marvelous treatment" she received. Dr. Taylor visited three times a day, and even Dr. Hicks would drop by to see how she was doing. Mrs. Doryliss—"she was precious"—gave her a massage at least once a day, and she always had a full bath twice every day. She recalls Mrs. Bancroft, Mrs. Hicks, Miss Lukens, Mrs. Northington and Miss Kit Derstine, a young woman just recently out of nursing school, as they went through their shifts over her eight-week stay.

Mrs. Northington's two daughters came in for tonsillectomies, and one— Nan—"roomed" with Louisa. Louisa became so afraid Nan would fall off the bed as the younger girl struggled to consciousness after her ether anesthesia that the nurses had to calm *Louisa,* she recalls.

Another patient was a tiny baby girl suffering from malnutrition. Louisa remembers the devotion of the nurses who cared for her.

This lengthy term at the hospital didn't end Louisa Skoog Whitten's association with Doylestown Hospital. On April 6, 1943, she gave birth to her daughter, Karen, at Belmont Avenue with Dr. Brad Green as her doctor. She was treated at West State for back trouble, a broken wrist and pneumonia, and her husband, Leonard, spent time there in his final illness.

Remembering it all, she is quick to say, "I had excellent care."

Despite the space provided by the 1927 Swartzlander memorial and other renovations, the house at Oakland and Pine seemed to be shrinking. Mrs. Grace Bancroft, supervisor nurse, reported the 14-bed, 8-crib facility admitted 62 patients in June 1934—and still had 22 adults and children on July first. This month was also the first time, announced Mrs. Twining, that the hospital's returns were more than its expenditures. How satisfying that must have been! The obvious success of the hospital venture and its frequent crowding were now forcing the women of the V.I.A. and their supporters within the community to eye alternatives.

The committee reconsidered buying the Clark property to the rear of the hospital in January 1935—but no, even greatly reduced to $900, it was still "impractical from every angle." In 1936, the ladies decided not to make an offer on the lot next to the hospital, for which Mrs. Frank Swartzlander was asking $20,000. Still searching for solutions, the committee looked into and then rejected Dr. Walter's proposal to exchange his Maple Avenue house for the Oakland building and $10,000.

Midway through these exercises, the committee learned it was the beneficiary of a magnificent bequest from Isaiah W. Closson of Carversville, once a patient in the hospital. When farmer Closson's estate was settled and all other bequests paid, the V.I.A. eventually realized nearly $50,000. With such a gift, the committee raised its sights.

In November 1936 the committee asked John H. Elfman of A.C. Elfman and Sons, Doylestown, to present a plan to renovate the present building. Despite the "skill and ingenuity" he showed in his proposal, the severe limitations of the site became clear. The committee concluded that Elfman's $20,000 estimate could "be spent more advantageously for a new hospital." And with that, the women directed

"Help Emergency Hospital and Visiting Nurse Fund" read the painted banner hung across the center of town between Shive's Hardware and the Fountain House, first used to advertise the canvass of 1934.

Services Validated
"Mrs. Bancroft told of our x-ray showing up a thymus gland in a baby born in our hospital after Abington's x-ray had pronounced it negative. Jefferson Hospital verified our finding."
—from Visiting Nurse & Hospital Committee Minutes, September 1935

Isaiah W. Closson

According to a February 26, 1966, special supplement to the *Intelligencer,* Closson had been "a Carversville cattle dealer, who could sign his own name but barely read and write." He gave the hospital "its first and largest legacy that amounted to between $30,000 and $40,000. The legacy was presented to the hospital in 1935." Later documents set the total bequeathed at $49,827.24.

His will read: "All the rest, residue and remainder of my estate I give, devise and bequeath unto the Village Improvement Association, a Pennsylvania corporation, located at Doylestown PA, for the use of the Doylestown Emergency Hospital."

Isaiah W. Closson, 1932

him to negotiate on the committee's behalf to purchase lots from the estate of Miss Ellen D. Atkinson at Belmont Avenue and Spruce Street and to draw up plans for a new building not to exceed $25,000.

Negotiations complete, the V.I.A. purchased the Atkinson lots for $4,500 on December 1, 1936. Two months later, the committee chose the firm of A. Oscar Martin & Son to design the hospital and paid John Elfman for the work he'd done to this point. Mrs. Kerr, Mrs. Shive, Mrs. William C. (Sara Harvey) Newell, V.I.A. president Mrs. J. Purdy (Hannah E.) Weiss, plus George Hart, J. Purdy Weiss and H. Leroy Kister, formed the Building Committee to oversee this massive undertaking. Countless meetings followed as these leaders cautiously determined the scope of the project—what the community needed, what it wanted, what it could afford.

Doing it right

In March 1937 the Building Committee met with the architects and the V.I.A. Executive Committee. After discussing George Hart's report on patient counts for the previous five years and determining that the hospital should remain small enough that it would not become a financial burden on the community, the committee concluded it needed a 20-bed hospital and proposed to construct it using $25,000 of the Closson legacy. Fred F. Martin offered his firm's services to draw preliminary plans (at no charge) in case circumstances required the project be canceled.

Anticipating increased expenses, the V.I.A. began fundraising in earnest with the next annual canvass. Mrs. Kerr went on the stump for expansion of the hospital, speaking to local service clubs and kicking off a drive for $6,500—$1,500 more than in previous years. In July, a statement from the executors of the estate of a Eudora Keller

Cat Tales
"Mrs. Swartley reported having to have porch boards removed to take out a dead cat."
—from *Visiting Nurse & Hospital Committee Minutes, September 1935*

One for the Maytag Repairman
In April 1938 the hospital's Maytag "mangle" (electric ironer) was *again* out of order, requiring Clymer's store to *again* loan the hospital another while repairs were made.

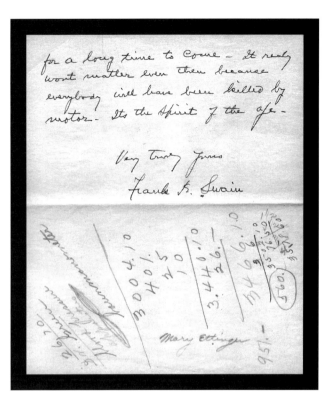

Frank B. Swain, manager of the Moravian Tile Works in Doylestown, enthusiastically supported the new hospital going up at Belmont and Spruce. He wrote "I think the present site for the Hospital is the best ever... And it's hardly likely it will be disturbed by making a highway of it for a long time to come— It really won't matter even then because everybody will have been killed by motor—It's the spirit of the age—"

revealed the hospital would receive approximately $12,000—another boost to the treasury.

The initial $25,000 estimate was quickly exceeded, once the architects began researching true costs and standards for a modern hospital facility. At a special meeting of the Hospital, V.I.A. Executive, and Building Committees in December 1937, Fred Martin "showed the attractive sketch of the story and a half, colonial-style hospital and the floor plan, explaining the three section divisions and giving an outline of interviews with doctors and surgeons and visits to eight hospitals [which he undertook before starting] on the 21-bed hospital plans." After asking questions and receiving a rough estimate of building costs as between $45,000 and $50,000, the committee granted unanimous approval. The V.I.A. confirmed this approval when it next met, and the project picked up speed.

The Hospital Committee figured it had about $43,000 available to build the new hospital: $37,000 of the Closson legacy and estimated proceeds from the sale of the old hospital. Following another special meeting, the interested committees recommended unanimously that the V.I.A. proceed with the approved building plans and award the construction contract to A.C. Elfman & Sons for the low bid of $48,754.99. Grateful for the assistance Mssrs. Weiss, Hart and Kister had given, the committee asked them to remain on the Building Committee to provide advice and guidance through construction.

The harder work

The months that followed involved the women on every committee in not only equipping and furnishing the new hospital, but hiring more staff, preparing the grounds, educating and involving the community in the project and raising money to pay for it. The contractors broke ground April 25, then laid the cornerstone May 28 with a reception that followed in Mrs. Twining's grove.

The Hospital Committee created a Nursing Technique Committee to establish better standards—it wanted to ensure that the skills of its staff and quality of its services measured up to the modern hospital it was building. Along with hiring new nurses and housekeeping staff, the committee prepared what appears to be its first true budget and set up, after several false starts, the salary schedule and fees for hospital services. In addition, it sought out donors and guided them through the process to equip and furnish the medical and patient facilities.

Mrs. Henry Douglas (Adele) Paxson contributed generously toward establishing and furnishing a laboratory at the new hospital in memory of her sister, Mary-Helen Warden Schmidt—initiating her

Louisa Kerr, Hospital Committee Chair, Speaks
"I have observed over a period of years that there have been many times when we *thought* we could not supply a bed to one or more patients, but as the times arrived a bed was available. In the last two or three years, however, there have been many times when the bed supplied had to be placed in the upper hallway or the office, or an extra cot or two in the ward rooms, and sometimes even in the kitchen for a few hours. Therefore our suggestion that we have outgrown our present quarters is based on the belief that we must be prepared to take care of the work which comes to us, in a proper manner, and to house the facilities for such work in a proper way. The x-ray machine and the sterilizer need to be taken from the operating room...The lift has been...greatly needed...so that our nurses and other such help as is available will not have to carry patients up or down the stairway."
—from her speech notes for annual canvass supper meeting, June 1937

60

Mrs. George W. Kerr, in polka dots, delivers address at cornerstone laying, May 28, 1938. From left: the Rev. Charles Freeman, A.C. Elfman, V.I.A. president Mrs. J. Purdy Weiss, John H. Elfman, Mrs. Kerr and John Stuckert.

long history of significant gifts to this "quite remarkable" hospital. J. Cecil Rhodes, of the Medical Arts Laboratory in Jenkintown, was granted permission to staff and operate the lab. The Hospital Committee agreed to provide the room, gas, electric and water, and either party could terminate the arrangement with reasonable notice given.

Keenly aware that this new facility would be more expensive to operate, the committee raised the 1938 canvass goal to $8,000. As individuals and organizations began to inquire about furnishing rooms at

In the late '30s, as the Hospital Committee considered the many issues it would face when it moved into the new, larger hospital facility from its renovated residence, it established a new committee to deal with quality improvement—and briefly called it Nursing Technique. As this committee's interests expanded, it soon evolved into a more elaborate structure in the new hospital.

After consulting with 16 local physicians, the committee developed this outline of suggestions—some of which now seem amusing or antiquated.

I. Supplies
   a. New or renovated gas machine
   b. Long stockings for patients in delivery room

II. Personnel and Duties
   a. Give clerical duties to a clerk so that supervisor may devote all her time to the nursing end of the hospital.
   b. Engage a graduate nurse who specializes in obstetrics for assistant to night nurse.
   c. Training in giving anesthesia and taking blood pressure.
   d. Maintain better discipline among nurses.
   e. Improve nursing technique
      1. more comprehensive charts
      2. written orders instead of verbal

III. Laboratory
   a. Majority of doctors would like a lab operated by a technician employed by the Hospital Committee rather than a commercial firm.

IV. X-Ray
   a. Films should be stamped with hospital's name.
   b. Doctor taking x-ray should not see patient after picture has been taken.
   c. Standard rates
   d. Expert should be employed to read pictures once a week.

V. Recommendations
   a. Invite Courtesy Staff of prominent outside physicians.
   b. Committee write a letter to each of the doctors using our hospital now urging them to use the new hospital more.
   c. Try to engage an outside supervisor to come to us three or four times a year to check up on the running of the hospital.

the new hospital, the House Committee investigated prices for equipment and furniture. The nurses were granted permission to collect money to furnish their own sitting room at the new site.

Business as usual

Meanwhile, the hospital, its staff and the Visiting Nurse Service had their work to do, too. In 1935 the hospital was licensed by the state Department of Welfare to accept up to eight maternity cases at one time. That November Dr. William I. Westcott—considered to be the town's first physician "specialist"—was granted permission to rotate in the call service for the hospital. The V.I.A. funded installation of a "bell system and speaking unit" to facilitate communi-

Last Twins in First Hospital?
On December 27, 1938, Fritz (Frederic Jr.) and David George Riley were born to parents Frederic and Louisa Riley of Edison, Bucks County. Fritz now lives in Applebachsville in upper Bucks and David in Mohnton, near Lancaster, PA.

COURTESY: HELEN L. ROBINSON

Moving from Pine and Oakland

Edna H. Greenawalt (1903–1994), past V.I.A. president, spoke about the early years of the hospital: "When we got it up to 16 beds, we thought we hit the roof!" She gives credit for the hospital's rapid growth and immediate success to the local physicians, noting that it was the support of the doctors who made sure "it was more than just a nursing home."

After the purchase of Pine and Oakland, at first the feeling was "we had this house, now what to do with it?" But, "sooner than we expected, we were overwhelmed with requests for overnights and had to move." It was an adjustment the V.I.A. found easy to make, since "we didn't consider the house a real hospital, and we wanted a *real* one."
—*from interviews conducted by Elizabeth Gavula in 1994*

cations through the hospital, and considered emergency lighting when a $600 estimate was presented. The hospital admitted 99 patients, assisted with 18 deliveries and conducted 50 operations in August 1936. After the new x-ray unit was installed in October—an $1,870 expense—"the supervisor cited the fine work the fluoroscope had done in a heart case." The Maennerchor Society donated an incubator to the hospital in March 1937, and it reportedly saved the life of Marilyn Cox Jones of Rushland who grew in its secure warmth from 3 pounds 2 ounces at birth to 6 pounds 5½ ounces when she went home. A new resuscitator brought another newborn "back to life." Mrs. Sophie Dietrich, the hospital's cook for a long enough period that her name actually appeared in the Hospital Committee minutes several times, requested a machine for making milkshakes…and two months later asked for a deep fryer. In October the Visiting Nurse Service began offering toxoid inoculations, probably for diphtheria or typhoid. When the new federal "44-Hour Law" went into effect,

History of the Property at Oakland Avenue & Pine Street

In 1827, Thomas Dungan bought 37 "perches" from Mary Shaw for $85. In 1842, the sheriff, Rutledge Thorton, sold Dungan's property, now with a stone house on it, to John B. Pugh for an unknown amount. The property turned over five more times before being sold to Frank and Susan Swartzlander in 1871 for $2,000. This would have been the first Dr. Swartzlander, father to Doylestown's Drs. Frank and Joe.

Dr. Swartzlander sold the house in 1890 for $2,805 to John B. Livezey, whose heirs sold it to Frank Swartzlander and William R. Mercer, trustees for the Doylestown Hospital Fund, in 1922 for $6,000. Mrs. Fretz built the addition to house the operating room, and the property was then transferred to the Village Improvement Association in 1923 for $1, after the V.I.A. had incorporated.

In February 1926 a new kitchen was added; the Swartzlander addition put a second story on the Fretz operating room later that year. When the hospital moved to its new quarters on Belmont Avenue in 1939, the Oakland building was sold to Julian and Elizabeth Gardy for $7,500. Willard and Sonia Rush purchased the house in 1974 for $45,000; it is now divided into apartments.

limiting the work week for non-nurse female employees, Mrs. Bancroft began to schedule work at the hospital to meet its requirements.

That summer was "one of busiest" Mrs. Pollock recalled in her years as visiting nurse, and the hospital followed suit: July showed 97 admissions, 22 deliveries, 42 operations and 23 x-rays. If the community and the hospital staff could hold on for a few months more, such numbers would not be a problem.

Dedication

The new hospital at Belmont and Spruce was complete except for a bit of grading and planting that would be tackled in the spring. Sitting on two acres at the east end of town, the impressive one-and-a-half-story red brick structure was surrounded by room for expansion. Its 31 rooms—two of them to remain unfinished—provided the community with a capacity of 21 beds.

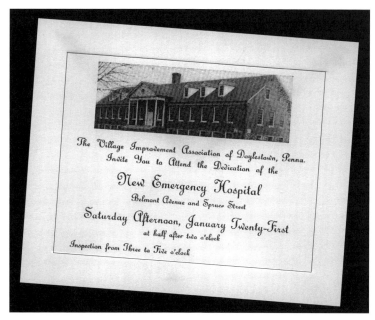

The total cost had grown to approximately $80,000, including $50,000 for construction, $25,000 for furnishings and equipment and nearly $6,000 in contributions of furnishings and equipment. The *Intelligencer* reported that, in addition to the Closson legacy, the hospital had recently received another bequest of $5,000 in the will of Frank Hart of Doylestown. The 1938 annual canvass yielded $5,500.

Approximately 2,000 visitors were on hand on January 21, a cold, clear Saturday afternoon, when Judge Calvin S. Boyer, Bucks County Courts, dedicated the new Doylestown Emergency Hospital. He declared that this event was "second in importance to no other local event in the entire history of this town and vicinity." Judge Boyer compared the growth of Doylestown's hospital with the development of the hospital "as a world institution and a mark of civilization.

"Not only have the founders shown their wisdom by biding their time and restraining their ambitions according to the means at hand," Judge Boyer said, "but they accurately gauged the peculiar needs of this community. There is an extensive area in the central part of Bucks County [where] there has been a crying need for hospital facilities.

"I now and hereby dedicate this Doylestown Emergency Hospital building to the saving of human life, the curing of disease, the healing of wounds and the amelioration of physical suffering. Long may it fulfill and carry on this sacred mission."

Dr. Sweeney, as chief burgess of Doylestown, spoke on behalf of the town: "From the citizens of Doylestown, this institution should receive the united support that it deserves. I know of no finer hospital of its kind and no finer monument to the progressiveness of the women of this community."

The dedication ceremony was opened by the Rev. Meyer M. Hostetter, pastor of Doylestown Presbyterian Church, and closed by

Celebrate, Then Back to Work

"The new Doylestown Emergency Hospital was formally opened to the public on Saturday afternoon January 21 [1939]. The weather was clear and cold. The architecture of the building so suitable to the town, the honest craftwork of the builders, the beautiful furnishings, the up to date equipment and many lovely flowers all combined to make the occasion a proud one both for the V.I.A. and the Hospital Committee, as well as the people of the town.

"At the close of the short, dignified and appropriate dedicatory services, visitors signed in the register, inspected the building and partook of a nice tea arranged for by Miss Gladys Hayman and her Hospitality Committee.

"At five o'clock the Hospital Committee had a brief meeting in the Health Center Room at which time on motion of Mrs. Kister, seconded by Mrs. Shive, it was voted that necessary lighting facilities needed for the wards and such as had been approved by Mrs. Bancroft, be purchased."
—Marie James Kister, secretary
—from *Visiting Nurse & Hospital Committee Minutes*

At the dedication, the Hospital Committee and other V.I.A. members posed for photographers around new anesthesia equipment. From the left: Mrs. William C. Newell, Mrs. Charles H. Shive, Mrs. George W. Kerr (chair of Hospital Committee, wearing corsage and bright smile), Miss Helen Ryan, Mrs. John Stover Fretz, Mrs. J. Harold Hoffman, Mrs. H. LeRoy Kister, Mrs. F. Cyrus Twining's nose and mouth, Mrs. J. Purdy Weiss (V.I.A. president, wearing corsage), Mrs. A. Oscar Martin (back) and Miss Ida Rodrock (in front of Mrs. Martin), Mrs. John C. Swartley, Mrs. Horace M. Mann, Mrs. Grace Bancroft, RN (hospital supervisor), Miss Laura C. Haines and Mrs. Harris Holmes. DOYLESTOWN HOSPITAL ARCHIVES

the Rev. A.B. Davidson, Doylestown Methodist Church. The new building was presented by the builder, Augustus Elfman, to the architect, A. Oscar Martin; Martin, in turn, presented it to Mrs. Weiss, president of the V.I.A.

Whether it was the weight of responsibility for this new and larger hospital or the thrill of achievement that drew them together again, the Hospital Committee felt compelled to meet the next day, a Sunday afternoon. The minutes of that meeting discuss a ramp that appeared to be too steep for safety and note that Amanda McKinstry—who would become one of the hospital's most warmly and universally loved employees—would start work on Tuesday.

T he wind pushed the cold in every chink, under every coat and pant leg, through blankets and woolen scarves. Lucky was the new mother who delivered the night before and would stay on with her baby at the old hospital with Mrs. Alice Brashears to care for her. They would have been cozy, tucked up together in the old emergency hospital while all the activity surged around them.

Wednesday, January 25, 1939, was moving day. The O.P. James ambulance was enlisted to carry patients the half mile from the original hospital building at Pine and Oakland to the new red brick hospital on the corner of Belmont and Spruce. The Fisher company moved furniture and equipment, helped by members of the Visiting Nurse & Hospital Committee—and their sturdy family members and volunteers from the community, as well.

Later on, with patients settled into their spacious, freshly painted rooms and the night nursing staff going about the accustomed business in a new environment, would have been just the time for a quiet tour of the building.

A walk through Closson's gift

T he front door opened onto a vestibule. Immediately to the right was the hospital office; to the left, a comfortable waiting room. Past these rooms, straight ahead, was the pantry, before which doors opened onto the maternity wing to the left—or east—and the medical-surgical wing to the right. A stroll down the new maternity wing corridor would take a visitor past the two-bed semi-private room, lavatory, four private rooms and a four-

Doylestown Emergency Hospital at Belmont Avenue and Spruce Street
DOYLESTOWN HOSPITAL ARCHIVES

Last Baby in the Old...

"Baby Has Own Hospital" states the headline on the fragile, yellowed newspaper clipping in the official Doylestown Hospital Scrapbook for 1939–40. That was the infant son of Mr. and Mrs. D. Byron Ely, New Hope, born Wednesday, January 18, who stayed at Pine and Oakland with Mom when the rest of the patients were transferred.

...First Baby in the New

"The new Doylestown Emergency Hospital's No. 1 baby arrived yesterday afternoon, just three days after the institution had been formally opened.

"The honor is possessed by a daughter of Mr. and Mrs. Robert C. Labs, Danboro, is the name of [sic] Nancy Closson Labs. She was named after the benefactor of the new hospital, the late Isaiah W. Closson, whose large bequest of money made the hospital possible.

"Baby Labs, weight 7 pounds, 13¼ ounces upon arrival, heads the new baby roll. Her brother, Robert Sherman Labs, was born Sept. 7, 1934, at the old Doylestown Emergency Hospital."

—*reprinted from the* Intelligencer, *January 27, 1939*

Hospital kitchen in the '40s
DOYLESTOWN HOSPITAL ARCHIVES

bed ward, and into the "working" area, where the glass-enclosed nursery, large washroom, labor and delivery rooms and sterilizing room assisted women in the business of bringing the next generation into the world.

The medical wing, no less important, would present to the visitor three private rooms and two four-bed wards before its corridor turned to the left. Along this extended the new Fretz Memorial operating room, then sterilizing room, x-ray room and accident receiving ward.

The ground floor contained an emergency power plant, health center, nurses' lounge, hospital kitchen and laundry, and the fully equipped laboratory funded by Mrs. Paxson.

Throughout the hospital were welcome gifts from individuals and the community in the form of beds, draperies, lamps, bureaus, linens, medical equipment, supplies, hand-crafted items, chairs, desks—the practical and the necessary side-by-side with the "merely" comfortable or comforting. While Isaiah W. Closson's legacy had made this particular move possible, the success of the hospital could be found most surely in the commitment behind these other gifts and financial donations, large and small, that supported the work of the hospital year in and year out.

Meet the employees

The hospital staff on opening day included Mrs. Grace Bancroft, superintendent of nurses and the hospital; day nurses Mrs. Helen Craig, Mrs. Reba Lukens and Miss Eleanore Shellenberger; night nurses Mrs. Lydia Doryliss and Miss Edythe VanArtsdalen; nurse's assistant at night Miss Sarah Histand; office secretary and part-time x-ray technician Miss Helen Bardsley; cook Mrs. Sophie Dietrich; laundress Mrs. Emma Reames; and janitor Charles Lewis. Part-time nurses and domestic help were involved from the start. One of the first of these was Mandy McKinstry, engaged to begin in the kitchen as the new hospital opened, who went on to become the heart of the maternity department and one of its most beloved personalities over the next 30 years.

However, one of the first tasks for the Hospital Committee was to hire a replacement for the superintendent, who had given notice. Meeting in the new Health Center rooms, the committee encountered the usual snags as it sought a suitable person for the post. Mrs. Hicks agreed to fill in while interviews for the new supervisor continued. In early April, Miss Margaret M. Allen came on board. She was efficient and capable, and quickly engaged the confidence of the committee.

A large part of Miss Allen's duties, as the United States entered the war, was finding and keeping nursing staff. By May 1943, the acute shortage caused her to request a special meeting of the committee, during which she announced that three of the nurses had resigned and a fourth may be forced to resign for lack of gasoline to commute. The committee opted to employ some of its clout in the community by conferring with the local rationing board for relief. It also decided it must inform the physicians that the hospital could take no more med-surg patients until the nursing crisis was resolved.

Advances in services

The X-Ray Department began in the new hospital under the supervision of Dr. Zulick and his assistant Dr. John A. Prickett, both of Abington Memorial Hospital, with fees for the service to be split with Doylestown Emergency Hospital. Mrs. Lois Stone began her 31-year tenure as a nurse and the hospital's first x-ray technician. Before the end of the year, the department grew busy enough that she would relinquish her general nursing duties to work exclusively for x-ray; within a few years, she had an assistant technician working with her.

Keep That Noise Down, Please!
According to an article in the January 21, 1939, *Intelligencer* on the "splendid new emergency hospital" dedication, the nursery on the east wing is soundproof.

Blue Bags
In May 1939, the minutes include the first mention of the familiar blue cloth bags, with "V. I.A." stitched on them in white, which volunteers carried when soliciting funds during the annual Visiting Nurse and Doylestown Emergency Hospital canvasses.

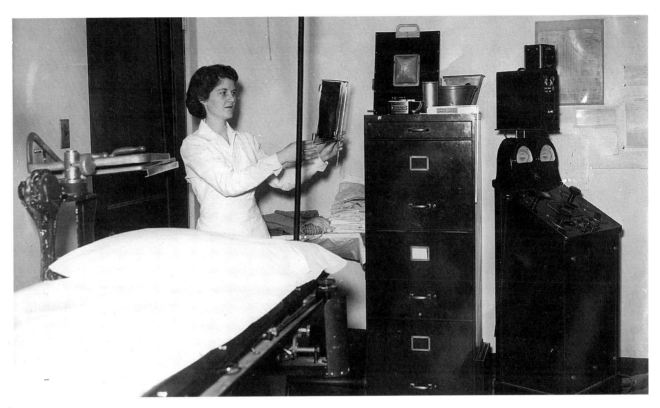

Lois Stone in X-Ray, 1943

The Veterans of Foreign Wars provided the full $1,800 needed to buy a newer reconditioned x-ray machine in late 1940, which allowed the old one to be converted to a mobile unit for bedside use. By this time, Dr. Prickett ran the department efficiently and at a profit to the hospital, with only a few complaints delivered by the doctors on the fees for the service.

The V.I.A. signed an agreement with J. Cecil Rhodes' medical laboratory in Jenkintown for Mr. Rhodes to run the new hospital lab in exchange for a percentage of the fees. While the arrangement served the hospital for a long time, it was one that never sat well with the physicians, the majority of whom felt the hospital would be better off operating its own lab with a doctor supervising. In 1940, the Hospital

Committee signed a new contract with Mr. Rhodes and Dr. Daman DeRivas of Lansdowne, who served as physician-director of the lab, which now came under nominal control of the hospital but actually was still run by Mr. Rhodes.

In May the lab was approved to conduct serological tests for syphilis under the prenatal and premarital laws, and later in the year, the lab was reappointed as the pneumonia typing station for Bucks County. Mr. Rhodes reported on a new blood typing process and a vaccine method developed to build up antibodies in donors for producing serum, and he suggested using the process with some of the local organizations that donated blood.

Red Cross and Visiting Nurse Service

Although the visiting nurse and hospital remained independent of one another, establishing the Visiting Nurse Service in its own rooms within the hospital permitted a closer association between the two. Mrs. Pollock told the committee the baby clinics had improved in the new quarters: the mothers appreciated the private examination room and seemed to feel freer to ask questions.

But for the other facets of her work—bedside care and educational programs—Mrs. Pollock's Red Cross supervisor suggested the visiting nurse might need an assistant. Not since the pre-hospital days had the job demanded more than one nurse—was it time to consider another? The committee hired a substitute to cover for Mrs. Pollock on the weekends, and soon the two nurses together were putting in about 60 hours a week.

In mid-1940, Dr. Harriet Davis—the area's first female physician—replaced Dr. Crough as baby clinic physician, and 22 physicians now worked with the visiting nurse.

Frightening Tales of Modern Technology, 1940
In March 1940, pipes in the kitchen, laundry, hallway and lavatories were covered with asbestos insulation.

The Cost of Canvassing
In August 1940, Mrs. Lucinda Harrold was reimbursed $2 for the doctor's bill and the cost of a pair of ruined stockings resulting from a dog's bite received while canvassing for the V.I.A.

Visiting nurses, circa 1950: Peg Emerson on left, Abigail Faust at the wheel, Jane Miller in white and Edith Kerwin

Doctors and techniques

Since the early days when a community hospital was still a dream for Doylestown, the area's physicians—beginning with Dr. Frank Swartzlander—had had a mighty impact on the committee and the development of the hospital. Gradually, the need had arisen to organize and tap into the potential of this growing group of professionals for the greatest good of the hospital and the community it served. The balance between yielding to every wish or opinion of any doctor and ignoring the wisdom and varied viewpoints they offered—this was one of many struggles that occupied the women of the Visiting Nurse & Hospital Committee every day.

When the committee announced in 1939 that the hospital could not handle and would not accept bookings for "semi-major" and "major" operations, a group of doctors protested. They assured the committee that it is the *physicians'* prerogative to determine how to handle each case and to be responsible for the outcome. The committee's motion to prohibit major operations was revamped to add "except in emergencies."

The committee reopened the issue of osteopaths using the hospital in January 1940. Mrs. Swartley moved to exclude them, but the motion died without a second. However, the exchange of letters between Mrs. Kerr and Dr. Hayman told a deeper story. The committee stuck to its previous policy, allowing osteopaths to perform no other surgery than circumcisions for their own maternity cases. Dr. Hayman withdrew his request to use the hospital for any of his patients, and Mrs. Kerr wrote on April 24 of her regret over his decision. "Speaking for myself," she closed, "I am looking forward to the time when your profession may be more fully recognized and accepted for its benefits to mankind." Tucked among these letters is an undated newspaper

Doctors in the Medical Records Room, 1954: Brad Green, William Lee, Redding "Fritz" Rufe   DOYLESTOWN HOSPITAL ARCHIVES

clipping announcing that Dr. Hayman had been issued a license by the state to maintain a private five-bed hospital and nursing home. In June, the committee invited Dr. Edward G. Drew, state-licensed osteopathic surgeon and chief gynecological surgeon at the Osteopathic Hospital, Philadelphia, to become a member of the hospital courtesy staff when called by local osteopaths for surgical cases.

Wartime hospital

Shortages of nurses, doctors, housekeeping help, gasoline, heating oil, food staples and fresh ingredients, plus blackout restrictions and salary ceilings—the war impacted the hospital in a multitude of ways. Windows were covered with new black drapes, two private rooms were converted to semi-private to accommodate increasing maternity cases, silk stockings—the perennial Christmas gift from committee to nursing staff for years—were simply unavailable. Facing the loss of so many doctors to the armed services, the committee was urged by Dr. Moore to appeal to the local draft board not to draft Drs. Green and Prickett.

First Female Pediatrician

Harriet Davis, MD, graduated from the Women's Medical College in 1935, did her internship at Philadelphia General Hospital, served as chief resident at Women's Medical, then came to Doylestown in October 1938. In 1942, when Dr. Westcott went into the Army, she took over his practice—then headed off to the Navy six months later. When she was discharged in 1946, she used the GI Bill to finance her education into pediatrics, taking her boards in 1950. By October 1948, Dr. Davis was back in practice in Doylestown as a pediatrician at 117 East Oakland Avenue, her office until her retirement in 1974. She was the first female, board-certified pediatrician in Bucks County (and the first pediatrician on Doylestown's staff) and only the second female physician in the county.

Dr. Davis seems refreshingly unpretentious regarding her role as the pioneering female among Doylestown's doctors. As she hearkens back to how the community responded to her in the '30s and '40s, she remembers with a chuckle that some women seemed critical of the "serviceable" hats she wore.

She worked with Hannah Pollock, took over the Well Baby Clinic from Dr. Crough when the Hospital Committee began rotating that duty and, later, became school doctor for elementary schools in the district. She recalls charging $1 for an office visit and $2 for a house call in her early years in Doylestown. Because she had experience with anesthesia and other procedures, she occasionally was brought in to help out at Belmont Avenue for tonsils and some gynecological operations. Dr. Davis was on call for the emergency room, just as the other doctors were, and she remembers it as an onerous duty that often interrupted treatments at her own practice. "If you had a roomful of patients, you still had to leave."

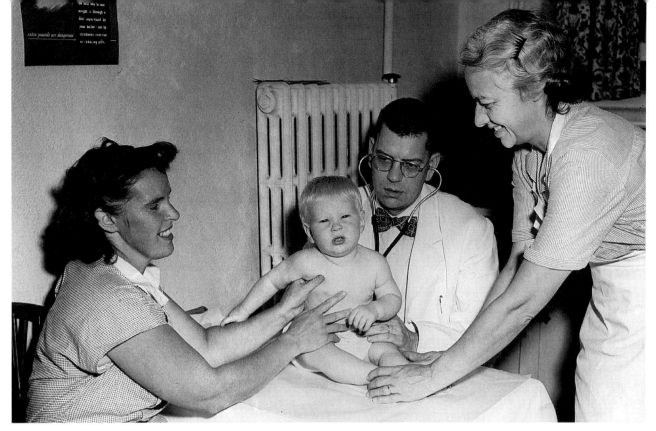

Dr. Sam Willard examines a patient at the Child Welfare Clinic, assisted by the baby's mother, left, and visiting nurse Mrs. Jane (Miller) Myers.

Mrs. Twining's Grove

F. Cyrus and Mary O.E. Twining purchased the Atkinson home, a large Victorian at Maple Avenue and Spruce Street that Mrs. Twining had always loved. There among her gardens she hosted teas and receptions for the Hospital Committee or served up cool beverages during warm summer meetings outdoors. Her daughter Betty later married Charles Kinney in the shelter of the magnificent weeping beech beside the house.

Good things happened, too, however. It was probably the war that brought Mrs. Lester (Pauline) Young to Doylestown Emergency Hospital in October 1942 as a private duty nurse for a friend. As legend has it, the friend went home but Mrs. Young stayed. The community mobilized to help stock the larder through the war, and it became a habit that continued long after the Armistice. In January 1943, the *Intelligencer* reported that 1,150 cans of fruit and vegetables, put up by different organizations, had been turned over to the Hospital Committee. When no other cook could be found, Mrs. James M. (Carrie) Shellenberger, past president of the V.I.A. and future Hospital Committee chair, offered to take charge of the cooking for patients and staff on Thursdays to relieve Mrs. Dietrich.

Miss Allen resigned her post as superintendent of nurses in early 1944 and was replaced by Miss Bertha Dinkelocker, a graduate of

The Methodist Hospital. She started her tenure just as Mrs. Shive and Mrs. Shellenberger began theirs as co-chairs of the Visiting Nurse & Hospital Committee after the death of Mrs. Kerr in late 1943. The three women stepped directly into the trenches, dealing with the ongoing struggles to maintain excellence in hospital care in the midst of staggering wartime growth and shortages.

That fall, the doctors met to form a "medical board," choosing Dr. Brad Green to represent them as "medical advisor" to the Hospital Committee. They expressed hopes for a children's ward and for a lab to be run by the hospital, not Mr. Rhodes.

Miss Dinkelocker suddenly folded under the pressure of the nursing shortage and the baby boom that filled the hospital in 1945. She resigned effective May 1, then fell ill, and Mrs. Young transferred from night nursing supervisor to day shift to cover for her.

Mrs. Young took charge smoothly and efficiently, as though she had been incubating such plans for years during the slow, hushed times on night duty. Within days of her appointment, she and Mrs. Brad (Harriet) Green, a trained nurse, assembled a group of married women who had previously been nurses to volunteer a day or more a week at the hospital. She found two nurses from Flemington to join the staff five days a week from 8:30 to 4:30. A commercial laundry would do the nurses' uniforms each week, up to four per nurse. She convinced the Hospital Committee to rent a room across from the hospital for out-of-town nurses to stay. Mrs. Keenan, the on-again, off-again anesthetist, was now scheduled for five days a week. Mrs. Young became instantly indispensable. The committee snapped her up for $200 a month, then fêted her with a welcoming tea in Mrs. Twining's garden on June 27, with all nursing and domestic staff invited.

Skills Where Needed

Mary Twining served as Hospital Committee treasurer for 25 years, retiring in June 1952. While her banker husband was presumed to have watched over her shoulder, she had obvious skills of her own. Long-time Hospital Committee chair Louisa B. Kerr knew short-hand (penciled loops and curves fill report margins and backs of envelopes in the archives), could write and deliver inspiring speeches to build support for the hospital's annual canvass, and knew how to draw the best from others. The ability to recognize skills the committees needed and to connect appropriate individuals to tasks was a valuable attribute of the V.I.A. leaders, then and now.

No Flies on Us, Part III

The committee approved the purchase in May 1943 of "electric fly swatters" from Sears, Roebuck, but what these may be is never determined, since Mrs. Mills reported the next month that she was "unable to buy them."

No Flies on Us, Part IV
The electrified screens just weren't doing a good enough job, so the committee considered spraying DDT, "now available to civilians," in September 1945.

More Tales of Modern Technology, 1945
Disposable diapers, under the trade name "Chux," were used for the first time on newborns at Doylestown Hospital.

Falsely Accused
Early in 1945, a Mrs. Earl White of Chalfont asked the Board of Health to shut down Doylestown Emergency Hospital, claiming it had an unacceptably high infant mortality rate. The hospital countered with its own records: of 371 babies born April 1, 1944, to April 1, 1945, just three newborns had died. One was malformed and two were premature births. The Board of Health commended the hospital for its fine record.

Expanding already?

I n 1940, after the hospital was approved for reimbursement from both Abington and Inter-County hospitalization plans, more patients began using Doylestown's facilities. By 1945, the baby boom was in full swing. The need for a children's ward was, at times, desperate. Pressed by critical overcrowding—maternity patients overflowed into halls and the med-surg wing—in 1946 the committee began evaluating options for enlarging the hospital. It examined several plans with architect Fred Martin of A. Oscar Martin & Son and consultant John M. Hatfield, administrator of Pennsylvania Hospital. Mrs. Young and the doctors also conferred with the Building Committee. Mr. Hatfield recommended taking a long-range view and planning for an eventual 100-bed hospital to serve 30,000, since the community was growing steadily. He also suggested, after conferring with Grand View and Quakertown Community Hospitals, that Doylestown raise its rates so as to be in a position to support a facility of the size the committee was considering.

Meanwhile, 23 doctors met on February 16, 1947, to form the hospital's first departmental medical staff structure: a medical board to govern surgical, medical and obstetrical departments, with Dr. Brad Green as chairman and Drs. Moore, Ward, Prickett and Lee as officers. The board played a big part in running the hospital and advising the V.I.A. and Hospital Committee. When the committee requested that new mothers and babies be kept in the hospital for a full seven days, Dr. Green responded on behalf of the medical board that the length of stay is governed solely at the discretion of the attending physician and that the hospital is unable to stipulate the length of stay in any case.

Mrs. Young continued to work her quiet magic. At her suggestion, the hospital changed to a five-day, 12-hour-a-day work week for her nurses in January 1946. When she later recommended an eight-hour shift schedule (7 to 3, 3 to 11, 11 to 7), the committee approved it, to begin August 1, 1947. It was Mrs. Young who told the committee the hospital facilities were capable of handling major operations, thus causing it to lift that prohibition.

Mr. Hatfield and Mr. Martin cooperated to develop designs based on the requirements cited by the doctors, the Building Committee and Mrs. Young. A single-story plan encroached on the adjoining Twining property; a two-story addition was beyond the committee's ability to build, maintain and manage. Not until April 1949 did the committee agree to a plan: a T-shaped two-story wing that mimicked one originally intended when the building was erected a decade earlier. The V.I.A. undertook the $225,000 project, which included extensive renovation of the current facility, and began raising funds. A.C. Elfman

1948–49 Officers and Sub-Committees Doylestown Emergency Hospital

Mrs. James Shellenberger
Chair

Mrs. LeRoy Kister
Recording Secretary

Mrs. Calvin Boyer
Corresponding Secretary

Mrs. Cyrus Twining
Treasurer

Mrs. Norman Lear
Assistant Treasurer

Finance
Grounds
House Cleaning
Kitchen
Laundry
Sewing
Visiting
X-Ray
Gifts
House
Insurance
Laboratory
Personnel
Visiting Nurse
Linens
Purchasing
Public Relations

Nancy Closson Labs, first baby born in the Belmont Avenue hospital, helps 11 years later to lay the cornerstone of the newest addition.

& Sons broke ground December 27; on March 25, 1950, the date stone was laid. Thousands attended the grand opening of the new wing February 3 and 4, 1951; a lesser number turned out on June 22 and 23 to view the final renovations and expansion.

Cost for the entire project was $215,000 for construction and $75,000 for equipment and furnishings—more than three-and-a-half times the cost of the original building just 12 years earlier! Doylestown Emergency Hospital now offered 54 beds, two delivery rooms, two nurseries, children's ward, operating room, expanded x-ray and lab facilities, a larger accident unit, an apartment for a resident physician (if such were needed) and consultations, and rooms and baths for nurses to use in inclement weather.

While this building project must certainly have made the

hospital as large as it needed to be for a long time, the committee continued to look ahead: it bought the adjoining 190 x 270-foot Darlington lot in June 1951 for $6,500—with the provision that Hillborn Darlington could keep a 50 x 100.5-foot piece adjacent to his Maple Avenue property to use for a garden.

Farewell to Miz Polly

Mrs. Pollock, who had devoted her life to the Visiting Nurse Service, resigned March 1, 1946, after a bout of illness. Although the committee accepted her resignation, it could not fill her place, and so she returned to duty at a reduced level of involvement. She resigned again—this time for good—in October 1948. For 27 years, with a few years off after her marriage, Hannah Haddock Pollock had been *the* visiting nurse to residents of the borough and surrounding townships. During her recent illnesses, the Visiting Nurse Service had cut back on its programs; even with two

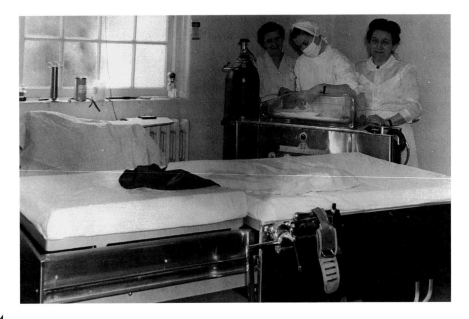

In the delivery room, 1949: From left, nursery aide Mandy McKinstry and RNs Elizabeth Mae Crooke and Ethel Faunce look over their newest infant.
DOYLESTOWN HOSPITAL ARCHIVES

Mrs. J. Harold Hoffman, Mrs. James M. (Carrie J.) Shellenberger and Mrs. Fred (Emily) Martin open the 1950 Hospital Committee fund drive.

DOYLESTOWN HOSPITAL ARCHIVES

Staff Notes, 1951

With the opening of the new wing and renovated main building, the nursing staff stood at 23 nurses, 3 orderlies and a "good many" relief nurses, said Mrs. Young.

part-time nurses, Mrs. Jenny Haney and Mrs. Jane Miller, taking over, the service took time to recover its vitality.

In January 1952, Mrs. Abigail Faust, a full-time trained Public Health Nurse, was appointed director of the Visiting Nurse Service. Shortly after, a county health department—one of the first in the commonwealth—was established for Bucks County. From the beginning, the VNS worked closely with the health department, for years representing the BCDH (Bucks County Department of Health) nursing services in the Central Bucks area. In 1954 the VNS employed four nurses responsible for the borough and 18 townships and began to make follow-up visits to patients discharged from the hospital. The service also offered prenatal classes, held "cancer detection clinics" in cooperation with the American Cancer Society and established a second Child Health

Clinic in Warminster that operated with the Doylestown clinic under the VNS until the county took them over 10 years later.

The Visiting Nurse and Hospital Committees operated under one umbrella within the V.I.A. structure until 1957, when separate V.I.A. committees were established. That fall, the BCDH asked the V.I.A. to supervise the work of the newly created nursing service: nurses employed by the county assumed responsibility for most public health matters, while V.I.A. nurses conducted bedside care. Gail Faust supervised both services.

Operations grow up

As the committee made major changes in the hospital's physical structure, it also revamped operations where needed. After years of growing dissatisfaction, in the fall of 1948 the hospital finally resolved its difficulties with the lab. It hired Dr. Gregory Froio of Hahnemann Hospital to supervise the lab, replacing Dr. DeRivas. By December, the hospital had given Mr. Rhodes notice. Dr. Froio added to and updated equipment in the hospital's lab at a cost of about $3,000, and then headed it, assisted by technicians Miss Portia Davey and Miss Florence Jacoby. The hospital carried the capital expense; monthly expenses and profits were shared between Dr. Froio and the hospital. The physicians were pleased. Drs. Hicks and Rufe donated their lab equipment. Within months, the lab was operating at a greater profit than it had ever realized, and with far fewer complaints or problems. By the mid-'50s, George Madara had become chief lab tech, assisted by part-time and full-time techs—including his wife, Doris—and pathologist Dr. John McGraw directed the department. The lab had finally become what it was envisioned to be.

In the X-Ray Department, the committee replaced the 10-year-

Doylestown, Pa., *November 22* 19 *45*

M. *rs. Dorothy Scheingold*

DOYLESTOWN EMERGENCY HOSPITAL

DOYLESTOWN, PENNA.

	To HOSPITAL ROOM AND CARE $\frac{5}{6}$ DAY, at $ 4.00 7.50 6.00		86	00
	From 11/7/45 To 11/22/45			
	To OPERATING ROOM FEE		10	00
	To ANAESTHETIC		10	00
	To MEDICINES		.5	50
	To X-RAY			
	To NURSES' BOARD			
	To LABORATORY FEE		18	00
	To TELEPHONE			
	To DRESSINGS			
	To AMBULANCE			
	To DELIVERY ROOM			
	To BRACELET		1	00
	To COT			
	To GUEST TRAYS			
	To VISITOR'S MEALS			
	To Special Laboratory Products			
	Penicillin		17	50
	TOTAL		148	00
	On account 11/2/45		40	00
	Balance		108	00

Not Responsible for Valuables Unless Checked at Office

Bills Payable on Presentation (One Week in Advance) Report Any Inaccuracies at Office Promptly
Received Payment
DOYLESTOWN EMERGENCY HOSPITAL
By *Mrs. Young*

Date *11 - 22 - 45*

This bill, signed by Mrs. Pauline Young, covered the cesarean-section delivery of Dot Scheingold's daughter Aida. Operating room, anesthesia, penicillin for Dot's "bad cold," and some two weeks of maternity care pushed the total to $148—high for 1945.

COURTESY DOROTHY SCHEINGOLD

Tea at Two

The Hospital Committee held a tea at the James-Lorah House Thursday, June 18, 1959, in honor of six employees who had been at the hospital the longest time: Mrs. Hannah ("Mother") Morgan, cook; Miss Mandy McKinstry, maternity; Mrs. Ruth Cramer, head of housekeeping; Mrs. Emma Wintyen, laundress; Mrs. Lois Stone, x-ray technician; and Mrs. Pauline Young, supervisor of nurses and of the hospital.

old equipment, which had reached the end of its life expectancy, when Dr. Prickett advised in 1950 that the Federal Communications Commission would outlaw the old equipment in 1951. The final bill for refitting the department came in just under $20,000.

With such upgrades common around the hospital, the Hospital Committee applied for accreditation by the Joint Commission on

Volunteer nurse's aides in 1953: Mary Gilmore, Peg Means, Mary Heath, possibly Thelma Neppes, Fran Cole

Accreditation of Hospitals (JCAH, now Joint Commission on Accreditation of Healthcare Organizations) in June 1953. As a first step to achieving this, a permanent, departmentalized medical staff was established with Dr. Allen H. Moore as the first director, replacing the medical board created six years earlier under Dr. Brad Green. Two years later, Doylestown Emergency Hospital was awarded accreditation and began the rounds of regular inspections by the joint commission.

A pleasant offshoot of accreditation came when the Ford Foundation granted funds to every accredited hospital—Doylestown's award, based on number of beds, was $29,700. This allowed the committee to add a morgue—which enhanced the hospital's standing for further accreditation. At that time, a generous legacy

**Signs of the Times,
June 1958**
To discourage patients from using the accident ward in lieu of a visit to the doctor's office, the committee raised the minimum fee to $3, effective immediately.

Some Things Change
This document was attached
to the Visiting Nurse &
Hospital Committee Minutes.

**Employment Policies for Professional Nurses,
Undergraduate Nurses, Paid Aides**
Approved Aug 30, 1954
presented by Mrs. Young, superintendent of hospital

- A 40-hour week prevails for all nurses.

- Three paid holidays each year, though not always on the holiday itself.

- General duty nurses receive 2 weeks paid vacation per year after one year of service; two years service, 3 weeks; six years, 4 weeks.

- Vacations do not accumulate beyond calendar year.

- Paid terminal vacations are granted after 12 months of service.

- Two weeks sick leave with pay per year. Sick leave may be accumulated to 30 days after two years service. Proof of illness must be established. No sick leave granted until after 6 months of service. No sick leave granted to pregnant nurses.

- One meal is allowed during each tour of duty. A 15-minute breakfast for 7-3 shift.

- Uniform laundry is provided by hospital, limit of three uniforms per week.

- Smoking on floor or diet kitchen is not permitted. This is a policy of the hospital and must be enforced.

- Nurses and Aides must go on and off duty to nurse in charge. One-half hour is allowed for meals. Days off must be taken when scheduled— they must not be changed from schedule.

- Resigning: a two-week written notice is required for Nurses and Aides to obtain a good reference or to be re-appointed in old position.

- Leave of absence to nurses to care for friends will not be permitted. A leave of absence will be granted where nurse or immediate family is ill.

- If a holiday falls within the vacation period, a day will be added to vacation time.

- Evening shifts receive $5 additional pay. Night shifts receive $10 additional pay. The pay period ends the 15th and last days of month; checks will be issued on the 2nd and 17th of the month. New staff employees will receive three $5 increases at 6-month intervals, which will be granted on Sept 15th and March 15th after six months' full-time employment.

from Mrs. Eugene (Kate P.) Shuman, a charter member of the V.I.A., provided the funds to build a service building, completed in 1956, to house the heating plant, laundry and a much-needed meeting room.

In April 1956, 36 doctors attended the annual medical staff meeting. They elected as officers Dr. Rufe, president; Dr. Russell Green (no relation to Brad), vice president; Dr. Prickett, secretary-treasurer; Dr. Lee, chief of the surgical committee; Dr. Westcott, chief of the medical committee; and Dr. Brad Green, chief of the ob/gyn committee. Ever thrifty, the Hospital Committee expected the doctors to purchase the board room chairs, and so far 20 doctors had paid for their own seats.

New beginnings

Mrs. Shellenberger retired as Hospital Committee chair in 1956, having ably led the committee through the struggles of the later war years, a major building project and innumerable internal and organizational changes. Her successor was Mrs. C.A. (Jane) Sienkiewicz, fresh from a term as V.I.A. president and a proven leader.

The improvements of the first half of the decade brought the hospital reaccreditation in 1957. This year, Doylestown Emergency Hospital elected to drop the "Emergency" from its name in light of its planned expansion into new medical services and surgical procedures.

Soon, the committee was examining fresh options, as it became apparent that the community was forcing the hospital to outgrow its space. This time, it undertook a three-year, $1.5 million building drive, bringing onto the steering committee two well-known Bucks Countians, author and native son James A. Michener and playwright and lyricist Oscar Hammerstein II. While the ambitious campaign fell

More Signs of the Times, June 1958
When the Blue Cross Hospitalization contract came up for renewal, the committee noted that the previous year's loss from Blue Cross patients amounted to $24,000.

Budget, 1959–60

INCOME	
$426,072	Patient Service
5,000	County Commissioners
2,215	Trusts
216	Free Bed
$433,503	Total Income

EXPENSES	
$ 61,414	Administration
26,900	Plant and Grounds
45,000	Drugs
13,284	Housekeeping
61,500	Kitchen
26,100	Lab
13,000	Laundry
116,750	Nurses
4,800	Interns
14,500	Orderlies and Janitor
20,400	Anesthetists
1,275	Record Room
23,580	X-Ray
5,000	Plant Fund for Capital Expense
$433,503	Total Expense

Brand-new baby, brand-new incubator, under the eyes of Mrs. Carrie J. Shellenberger, Hospital Committee chair, and Mrs. Pauline Young, director of nursing

The Search Begins: October 1959

Mrs. Matthew (Prue) Suydam, chair of the Professional Affairs Committee, suggested the newly expanded hospital would need "a well-trained worker in hospital administration, not just a successful business manager." The committee agreed, and further directed that such a person be hired before the new wing was completed.

The Search Ends: January 1960

The hospital committee hired Jaromir Marik, 34, assistant administrator at Pennsylvania Hospital, at a salary of $8,000 after the Professional Affairs Committee interviewed six of 13 applicants for the job.

short of the goal, community support was remarkable. To raise sufficient funds to qualify for federal aid under the Hill-Burton program, schemes were devised by service clubs, fraternal organizations, teenagers, children, hospital personnel and V.I.A. members—much in the spirit of the decades-earlier push to fund the visiting nurse, emergency rooms and first hospital. This enabled the hospital to go ahead with about half of the projected addition, and on March 8, 1959, the hospital broke ground again.

In the midst of *this* building project, the Hospital Committee faced the realization that, after 36 years, it could no longer maintain the quality it wanted in its hospital, administered by a committee of non-professional volunteers. Its subsequent search yielded a young, experienced hospital administrator, Jaromir Marik. As the decade closed, so did an era.

T he summer after Jaromir Marik was named assistant administrator at Pennsylvania Hospital under H. Robert Cathcart, he and Bob drove through Doylestown on their way up the Delaware River to a three-day canoe trip paddling downriver to New Hope. The beauty of the town and countryside impressed him greatly. A few months later Mrs. Matthew (Prue) Suydam, chair of the hospital's Professional Affairs Committee, wrote Bob Cathcart on the advice of Dr. Vic Fredrickson, a local doctor, to ask for help in finding an administrator for Doylestown Hospital. Cathcart responded to Mrs. Suydam's letter on Jerry Marik's behalf, "and that's how I came to the hospital," Marik notes.

Driving north on Route 611 to his interview in Doylestown on an overcast, snowy day, approaching the town across the wind-driven stretch of fields—all there was between Warrington and Doylestown in those days—he saw few cars, no heavy traffic and a town "out in the sticks, and that appealed to me."

Just as the 34-year-old Marik was looking for a hospital of his own to administer—and a meaningful personal and professional challenge— the committee was seeking an experienced, dedicated, adventurous cohort who would head the hospital's family of employees and be able to support, assist, advise and, when called for, lead the strong-minded, independent, capable women of the V.I.A. and its Hospital Committee in the running of this community hospital. Would it be possible, in 1959, to find someone able to respect, understand and cooperate with a group

The arrow points to the hospital at Belmont and Spruce in this photo of Doylestown, taken between 1965 and 1970.
DOYLESTOWN HOSPITAL ARCHIVES

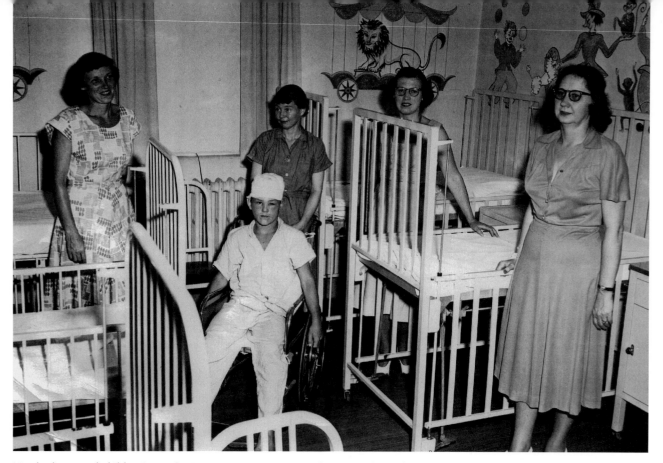

Newly decorated children's ward, 1960: Bert Linsenmaier Hellyer, president of Junior Woman's Club; Bill Means in wheelchair, first patient; Mary Twiford, JWC, artist; (Anne Chestnut, JWC, artist, not shown); Alta Holmes Ennis, JWC; Lucinda Harrold, V.I.A.

of accomplished women? And from Marik's viewpoint arose this concern: Could the Hospital Committee relinquish its day-to-day management of the hospital to *any* man or woman?

The Professional Affairs Committee chose Marik from six applicants they interviewed. In January 1960 the Hospital Committee supported the recommendation. Mr. Marik, as he was always called by the employees and most of the committee for the next 30 years, sat in on his first committee meeting February 29 and became, in time, as much a part of Doylestown Hospital as the women themselves.

In 1960, the hospital organization was simpler than it would ever be again. Technology, medicine, governmental regulations, laws—these were changing rapidly, affecting hospital operations in ways neither the women of the committee nor the businessmen and doctors of the community could have envisioned 20 or 30 years earlier. With the coming of its first professional administrator, the hospital took a leap ahead that opened it to the influence of the outside world in unprecedented ways. Would it be able to retain its small-town, "family-run" feel and offer the up-to-date healthcare services people needed, with a paid administrator as buffer between the hands-on women and the staff— or between the women and the patients? The community watched for signs of a new hospital emerging from this major alteration to the management structure.

Building and assessing

J erry Marik came on board in the midst of phase one of the extensive building project planned in 1957. "That was one of my first tangible jobs: to see to the completion of the project, equip it and prepare for the opening." The new construction stretched the front of the hospital along Belmont Avenue to the east, and added a new front door. The wing rose a full two stories and extended back toward the Darlington house lot.

On May 1, 1960, the new wing was officially opened and 1,400 people toured the business office, two floors of med-surg units, the pediatric ward and the first gift shop and snack bar—which, notes Marik, "remained forever one of the pearls of the V.I.A.," committing its substantial profits to the Building Fund. Mrs. Earle A. Brown, president of the Pennsylvania Federation of Women's Clubs, and Miss Bertha Adkins, undersecretary of the Department of Health, Education & Welfare in Washington, DC, spoke at the dedication, along with local dignitaries.

While the construction project was nearing its conclusion, Marik evaluated how the Hospital Committee functioned and how it meshed with the staff and departments. By assessing the organization in advance, he hoped to avoid making changes he might regret later.

His evaluation revealed that each of the departments had organized itself in its own way. There were no standardized pay schedules, and employment policies varied. "One of my priorities," Marik says, "was to get the hospital to pull together, and for all personnel to be treated equitably. That took some time."

By the early '60s, Doylestown Hospital had approximately 50 to 60 physicians on staff. With the exception of the radiologists,

1966 Medical Staff: seated, B. Green, Richie, Schumacher, Simpson, Ricker, Shetzley, Ichter, Laudenslager, Davis, Rufe, Conahan; standing, Darnell, Mazaheri, Shoenthal, Bulkley, Brenneman, Pershing, Garner, Wagner, Leiby, Willard, Monteith, Haeckler, Burmeister, Peters, Fox, Morrison, Weeder, R. Green, Frank, Bassert, Bucher, Souilliard, Gribb, McGraw.

pathologists and others contracted with the hospital to perform services, most of the specialists were then, as they are now, in private practice.

"My job, as I saw it, was to make sure the patients received the services they came into the hospital for." And so, another of Marik's goals was to determine a way to work with the medical staff and make it accountable, individually and collectively, for the services the physicians performed in and for the hospital.

"Work with the medical staff caused me more sleepless nights than anything else." Marik found he had more success if he dealt with the physicians "more by persuasion than by edict."

Growth of specialization

Through the '60s and '70s, Doylestown Hospital accomplished its transition into specialized medicine. The doctors began the process by developing their areas of interest and experience, achieving the training and earning certification. The development of the departments followed that process, compelled by the needs of the fast-growing community and propelled by medical advances.

Dr. Brad Green had opened his practice in Buckingham in 1935. Until 1946, he had been the only full-time, registered surgeon at the hospital. Through the 1960s, Doylestown was primarily a maternity and emergency hospital, and with Dr. Green's particular interest in obstetrics—and the war's impact on the birth rate and availability of physicians—he had become a critical member of the staff. When the staff began to organize, Dr. Green headed it; later, when the departmental staff structure was formed, he was named chief of ob/gyn—though never certified for the specialization. Such an appointment was common practice for rural areas at a time when credentialed specialists were available primarily in city settings.

For Dr. John Gribb, board eligible in obstetrics when he opened his practice in Doylestown in October 1959, the next decade marked a period when obstetrics and gynecology were "evolving into a true department." At first, he wrote rules and regulations at Dr. Green's request. Later, he designed an obstetrical-gynecological-prenatal record and devised a system for categorizing physicians and privileges based on experience, training and certification. Certified in 1964, Dr. Gribb was joined by Dr. John Choby (still practicing in 1998) in 1969, the same year he moved up to department head upon Dr. Green's retirement. "I think the department of ob/gyn really began after the other obstetricians started to come," he says.

Other departments were established in much the same way. Dr. William I. Westcott had come to Doylestown Hospital in 1935—

Making Do
Helene Bryan tells this story about her husband, Dr. John S. Bryan, Doylestown Hospital's first orthopedic surgeon: "He would go out to the barn and make instruments and contraptions to 'hang up' his patients," before manufactured traction apparatus was widely available.

Family Practice Cycle

"At the close of World War II, the family physician is *the* physician. There are no specialists except in the very big city hospitals," explains Dr. Edwin Knopf, the hospital's current vice president of medical support services and unofficial medical staff historian. "After the war the specialties of medicine generally matured and demanded special training programs. That specialist history did not reach Doylestown, however, until the mid '60s when we began to get internists—super-specialized medicine, more detailed training than the general practitioner. A number of our first specialists were GPs evolving into specialists. By the '70s, practically all new physicians settling here were specialists, and we began to get more depth to the medical staff.

"Unique to Doylestown Hospital, we never gave up on the general practitioner," says Dr. Knopf. "While other hospitals began to push out general medicine and the family docs, our position has always been that as long as a physician was capable of doing 'x,' he could do hospital work 'x.' As long as Dr. [Charles] Burmeister was capable of taking care of newborns, he had that privilege."

In time, many generalists who chose to remain generalists gave up ob/gyn, internal medicine and other specialized fields because they didn't have time and because malpractice insurance drove them out. This fueled the growth of specialties, almost to the point of having too many specialists, but that has abated as family practice has evolved into a specialty of its own, filling a desire for more grounded, holistic care to complement the specialties. And again, insurance—this time, health insurance—has played its part in developing the trend.

Pat Zilli in the kitchen, 1960s DOYLESTOWN HOSPITAL ARCHIVES

and had practiced as a general practitioner-internist, although he was not certified or formally trained in internal medicine. When Dr. Richard Vanderbeek (still practicing in 1998) joined Westcott, Dr. Rich Schumacher—the town's first board-certified internist—and the hospital staff in 1964, Dr. Vanderbeek was only the second doctor certified in internal medicine to practice at Doylestown. "When I came, it was basically a hospital run by GPs."

Having trained at Abington Memorial Hospital, Dr. Vanderbeek had adopted that institution's belief that the general practitioner is an important cog in the delivery of health care, and he carried that into his practice at Doylestown. "Once the GPs realized that when they sent us patients, we'd treat them and send them right back," this working cooperation between general practitioners and specialists became one of the hospital's greatest strengths.

In the '50s, board-certified doctors came up from city practices to serve on staff at Doylestown part-time. Dr. William Lee, surgeon, initially had given a day a week to Doylestown's operating room; later he became a full-time member of the medical staff. Dr. Alexander J. Michie, urologist, saw patients at Doylestown sporadically; but then he brought Dr. Ahmed Mazaheri, a young associate, into the hospital in 1962—and Dr. Mazaheri stayed, with the specialty of urology forming around him.

Meanwhile, Mrs. Young became director of nursing in mid-1961, a new title that reflected the shift toward making hospital operations more departmentalized and more efficient. Her duties changed further as the development of other departments and services allowed her to relinquish some responsibilities—and as the growth in the nursing staff required more of her expertise as its manager.

Visiting Nurses rejoin hospital community

In 1960, the Visiting Nurse program received an annual income of $5,000 from the estate of V.I.A. member Martha Dana Mercer, who had been vitally interested in the service since its inception. The next spring, it instituted the Homemaker's Service, which operated successfully for three years until the county commissioners introduced the Bucks County Homemaker's Service.

In April 1964, the well child clinics of Doylestown and Warminster came under the full responsibility of the county, while the Child Welfare Committee of the V.I.A. continued to do volunteer work. With this, the Visiting Nurse Service ended relations with the Bucks County Department of Health, feeling it could give better service, particularly to the elderly, as a private agency under the auspices of the V.I.A. The visiting nurses relinquished all public

Bloomin' Flowers

For 40 years, the Peter Hellberg Company, Chalfont, brightened the rooms, lobbies and corridors of the hospital with regular donations of cut flowers from its nursery. In more recent years, Jane, a V.I.A. member, and Joe Hellberg and their family have continued to support the hospital in many other ways. Jane served on the Hospital Board from 1968 to 1974.

Former Hellberg employees Don Nehoda and John Trapp bought the business from the Hellbergs in 1994, and they have continued the tradition from Chalfont Growers. Each week, the hospital picks up leftover cut flowers that are then arranged by volunteers to bring cheer to those who work or visit there. Don, who began working at the nursery when he was 15 years old, says, "We're glad to do it, and I know the people up there like to see them—that's the reason we do it."

Budget, 1965–66

$1,172,183
$ 843,619 (72 percent)
is salaries and wages.

Send Out the Wash

The hospital contracted with a commercial laundry in June 1966, enabling it to do away with its own laundry department, which had been a fixture since 1923.

Trading Places

Martha Drapeau, retired Maternity nurse, remembers an evening she was called down to help out on one of the men's wards. The nurses were expected to get the patients settled, give each of them a relaxing back rub and, in short, tuck them in. But she had a surprise waiting for her when she came into the room. "It turned out they had been trading their teeth around! I had to get all five sets of teeth together in a basin, scrub them, and then try to fit them to the right mouths." She's not sure to this day if the right teeth left the hospital in the right mouths.

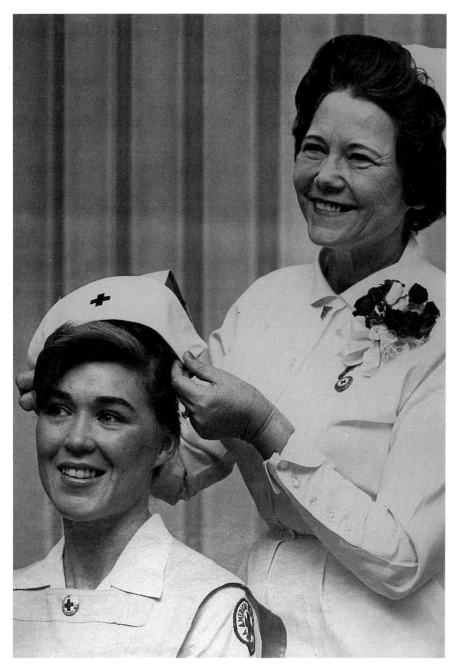

Mrs. Young places cap on volunteer nurse's aide, 1960s   DOYLESTOWN HOSPITAL ARCHIVES

The Christmas Shop operated seasonally for many years, beginning in 1960. In 1961, it sold its first mint toffee wreaths—and hundreds more for years after that. This gathering in February 1974 of the wreath makers includes, from left, Lu Brunner (who tied the bows on every wreath), Ginnie Sommerer, Alma Corson, Mrs. Edwin Brady (a community member who helped with the project) and Martha Sine. The men who helped tie candies to wreaths are Carl Bodhun, Russell Myers, George Leaworthy and Charles Miller (who made the wire wreaths).

DOYLESTOWN HOSPITAL ARCHIVES

But They Washed Them First!

Mrs. Edward O. Steeley made 1,400 stuffed dolls in the first 4½ years of the Gift Shop's existence, as announced in the *Volunteer's Voice;* Sarah Brady also stitched dolls to add to the shop's profits. According to long-time Gift Shop volunteer Martha Sine, the government later shut down production because the dolls had been stuffed with used nylons.

COURTESY: CAROLYN BACHMANN

health work and concentrated on what they did best: bedside care cases.

A year later, the Visiting Nurse Committee (VNC) began a free dental clinic for needy school children. Once it was firmly established and state funds were secured to assure its continuation, it was put in the charge of the school nurses.

Beloved Hannah Haddock Pollock died in 1965, just a year short of the 50th anniversary of the Visiting Nurse Service. Gifts to the VNS in Miz Polly's memory established a fund that still awards a prize to a graduating member of Central Bucks High School's Future Nurses Club who plans to enter a school of nursing. Later, the fund name was expanded to honor Laura Haddock, Hannah's sister, who taught school in Detroit before returning to Doylestown in her retirement.

Development in state and federal aid for medical expenses brought about a change in the structure of the Visiting Nurse Committee of the V.I.A. To meet certification requirements from the state health department for medical coverage, the VNC formed the Visiting Nurse-Home Care (VN-HC) Council. This linked the committee with the hospital's newly established Home Care Department, supervised by Mrs. Elizabeth Ackley, visiting nurse. State requirements for the whole program resulted in the rejoining of hospital and visiting nurse committees in summer 1968. Generous legacies received over the years, including those from Mrs. Mercer and Miss Laura C. Haines, were entrusted to the hospital treasurer.

In late 1969, the department grew again when, with the dissolution of the New Hope Public Health Nursing Service, Doylestown Hospital incorporated the service area into its VN-HC Department, making the patients in the new area eligible for services in the Medicare program. Doylestown Hospital also contracted with Bucks County Homemaker Service Inc. to provide home health aides to assist in exercises, administer medications, give personal services and perform certain necessary household tasks. Betty Ackley, director of VN-HC, coordinated the extended service.

Pushing out the walls

I n the summer of 1964, the hospital began the next phase of its planned building project. Since no existing facilities were shut down during construction, the potential for difficulties was great. Completing the original expansion plan took much longer than Jerry Marik and the committee had envisioned. With the hospital's daily occupancy through construction running close to—or exceeding—its official capacity of 85 beds and 18 bassinets, overcrowding was an additional problem.

On February 27, 1966, the open house to view the new addition ended 20 months of major construction-in-progress while the hospital functioned around carpenters, painters, masons, plumbers, electricians, roofers, engineers and architects. The result was reportedly pretty spectacular: new operating rooms on the first floor, an entirely new maternity unit on the new third floor, x-ray department, more med-surg rooms on the second floor, and an expanded dietary department/ kitchen in the basement of the 1960 addition. Temporary services were installed in the former operating and maternity areas until a final determination was made on how best to use the space.

A year later, the enlarged emergency department opened in the old operating area, and the former second-floor maternity ward housed the hospital's first intensive care unit—designated a "special care unit." Cardiologist Dr. Joseph McGarvey Sr. (still practicing in 1998) recalls starting this four-bed unit "with great excitement." Bed capacity rose to 129.

More Tales of Modern Technology, 1960: What Will They Think of Next? "Mrs. Gross announced a new piece of equipment called a duplicator had been bought. Its primary purpose was to take care of the menus, but it will have other uses." —from the Hospital Committee Minutes

Doylestown Hospital, circa 1968

Back in 1960, the Hospital Committee had approved six-year term limits on V.I.A. appointments to the committee, so when Prue Suydam assumed the duties of Hospital Committee chair upon Jane Sienkiewicz's departure in June 1966, she knew she had just six years to serve in this capacity. She probably didn't know, however, just what she was in for during her tenure.

No longer did the Hospital Committee and administrator plan and build an expansion—and then have the luxury of resting for a while to gather strength and accumulate data before the next challenge. The

Nursing Station, 1960s
DOYLESTOWN HOSPITAL ARCHIVES

complexity of every aspect of administration had grown to the point that overlap between projects was common. Nowhere was this more evident than with the consideration of how to grow the hospital as big as the community needed it to be.

"When we finished each expansion," Marik recalls, "I automatically began to think: What's the population projection? What's next?" In 1965, in the midst of construction, the committee hired a

A Voice Is Heard

A Voice Is Heard

The quarterly internal newsletter, *Volunteers' Voice,* was first published in March 1965. Its editor was Mrs. Edwin H. (Irma) Satterthwaite, who cheerfully spread the news of the hospital for 10 years before retiring. Mrs. Satterthwaite also started the first employees' publication, *Bare Facts,* in 1973. This forerunner of *The Enthusiast,* the present associates' newsletter, was named for a sketch by Edward Anklam that demonstrated the minimal coverage provided by hospital gowns!

May I Have This Dance?

The Stardust Ball began in 1965 and was held for several years to kick off the Junior Woman's Club's Village Fair, which ran successfully from 1962 to 1993.

hospital consulting firm, Agnew, Peckham & Associates of Toronto, to evaluate what it could accommodate on the Belmont site—as compared to relocating. By the fall of 1967, Agnew, Peckham's report pointed out that it would be *possible* to stay at Belmont and noted the drawbacks to doing so. Chief among these would be land on which to expand.

But then a powerful Philadelphia-area planning agency, the Hospital Survey Committee, discussed further the strategy of remaining on-site or relocating. It became clearer that by staying, the hospital would always be hampered. And so, despite the handful of lots purchased over the years with expansion in mind, the committee and Marik began to search for a new site and funding with which to build. With much open land still available in the Central Bucks area, the committee hired architect Alexander Ewing to help crystallize the criteria for a site.

Over the years, many local groups participated in the Village Fair to help support the hospital. These men of the Doylestown Rotary Club are planning their chicken dinner for the 1966 fair. DOYLESTOWN HOSPITAL ARCHIVES

According to Prue Suydam, "We looked at 33 sites. I don't think anyone realized how many angles we had to consider before choosing a location." She remembers that the Bucks County Planning Commission, headed at the time by Franklin Wood, seemed to take a personal interest in the hospital's decision to relocate and its subsequent site search. It advised the committee about population projections and the various site characteristics it must consider, chiefly a water source and good access to a major highway interchange. "We knew if we didn't relocate, some other hospital would build and we'd become a second-rate institution," she says.

Development of Doylestown's Emergency Department

Emergency Only
At first, only emergency care was offered. This was provided by visiting nurses and doctors, first in patients' homes and later in the rented emergency rooms.

Part-time Department
At Oakland Avenue from the beginning, round-the-clock staff cared for patients once they were admitted, but any "emergency room" there or at Belmont was staffed only as needed until the '60s. Nurses would take the patient into the emergency unit and notify the patient's own doctor or the doctor on call.

Staffed Emergency Room
As the hospital and the community grew, doctors were assigned or accepted rotating emergency room duty for which they were on call. Physicians remember that initially they were unpaid for this community service; later they received $25 a month.

Full-time Department
Finally, a fully staffed, 24-hour Emergency Department was established around 1975 at the new site on West State. It now has its own specialists in emergency care and is a separate unit of the hospital.

Get-Well Pillows
Mary Twining, long-time Hospital Committee treasurer, made and gave away more than 700 small, roll-shaped neck bolsters to recuperating hospital patients and new mothers between January 1956 and June 1963, according to records she kept. "Each pillow was delivered personally, often with a flower bouquet or a few cookies," recalls her daughter, Betty Twining Smith. Betty says the early pillows were made of feathers, which would occasionally drift down from the balcony of the Twining house adjacent to the hospital when Mary was busy working on her "pillow-making project."

Dietician Kathryn Haeflin,
Judy Mang and Lynn Gearhart
in the hospital kitchen, 1966

While the hospital looked for land, the Route 611 bypass was planned and construction began, splitting off a portion of the 70-year-old campus of Delaware Valley College on Route 202 and isolating two parcels along the new bypass to the west of town, in Doylestown Township. The hospital established contact with Dr. James Work, president of the college, to discuss the possibility of acquiring the 35- and 15-acre parcels to build a new, modern hospital for the community in this fortuitous location. This was not the only land the hospital committee considered, but as negotiations with the college continued into early 1969, it became the principal option.

More business as usual

Even as it was negotiating for the college land and exploring funding avenues, the Hospital Committee was carrying on the business of the hospital.

In 1967, Miss M. Anne Cameron, an RN from Abington, was named assistant director of nursing. Al Hertzler joined the staff as chief pharmacist. The Men's Advisory Committee, a non-voting group made up of 19 men from different parts of the hospital's service area, formed to provide insight and community participation in the operations of the hospital and to help the committee decide whether to remain at Belmont or relocate. A part-time social service department was established to assist Medicare patients with interpreting benefits. Jaromir Marik was named a fellow of the American College of

When Security Breaks Down for Good Reason

In the time before it was open around the clock, the doors of the hospital at Belmont were locked at night, requiring doctors, patients or ambulance crews to ring a bell at the Emergency entrance for a nurse to come down and let them in. Dr. Joe McGarvey Sr. tells the story of the night he was called in by the nursing staff to help with a patient in some distress. He arrived and repeatedly rang the bell, but no one came to let him in. With youthful resourcefulness, he tramped around front and found an unlocked window. He managed to shove it open, hoisted himself over the sill into the empty nurses' station on A-4, then proceeded down the hall to locate the nurses on duty with their patient.

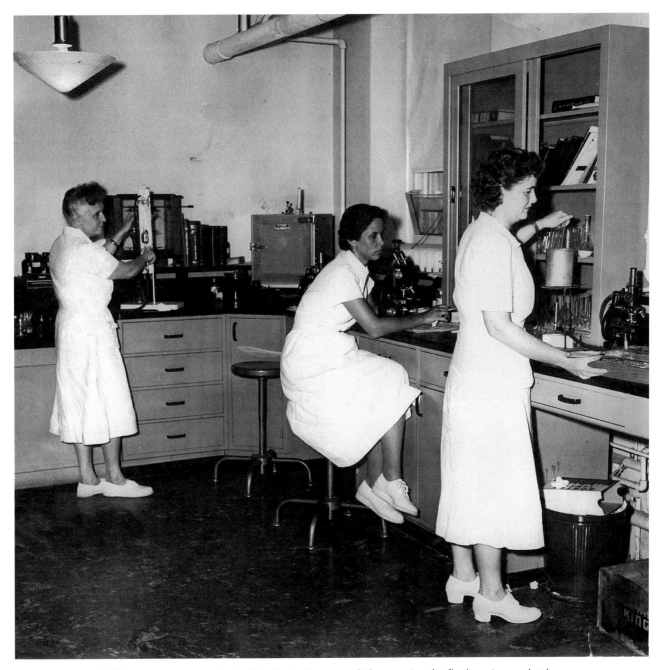

DOYLESTOWN HOSPITAL ARCHIVES

In the lab, Portia Davey and Florence Jacoby flank an incompletely identified "Miriam," 1960.

Hospital Administrators. The V.I.A. received one of many Benjamin Rush awards of the Bucks County Medical Society, this for completion of its building program.

Renovations to the original 1939 building began in 1968 to add office and lab space and to renovate the med-surg and emergency wards there. In December, the hospital's first triplets—three girls—were born to Mr. and Mrs. Robert M. Holbert of Doylestown with the help of Dr. Eugene Helsel.

Three Decades at Doylestown

Anne Boehringer, operations manager of the laboratory, has spent 30 years in the lab at Doylestown Hospital. At one time, she recalls, she and her coworkers received all their meals for free, and were paid 8 hours for a 7½-hour work day; she believes she started at $3.25 an hour. Anne worked in the basement on Belmont Avenue, "where water would pour in the window wells when it rained and snow would pile up inside if the wind blew a certain way." Often, she says, it was so cold they had to wear earmuffs and mittens inside.

"A blood sugar [test] that now takes seven minutes to analyze used to take two to three hours to run, and would only be done a couple of times a day. For emergency transfusions at night, we would call in donors, bleed them, process the blood and send it to OR. Talk about 'fresh blood'!

"I was hired over the telephone—no interview, no medical history, no orientation, no [continuing education], no CPR, no [required annual hospital education]...

"In 1964, we had one office clerk and three techs. I was the fourth one hired. There are now 63 associates in the lab. We took 'call' for a week at a time from 4 [p.m.] to 8 [a.m.]. We had an on-call room and sometimes never got home the whole week. The lab only staffed from 8 to 4:00.

"The RNs all wore caps—[there were] no LPNs or aides—and they started all IVs and EKGs, did all respiratory treatments, fed the patients, etc. Parties and gatherings included everyone from housekeeping to chief surgeon."

Gone, but Never Forgotten
In October 1969 Pauline Young retired. As "evidence of our affection and esteem," a portrait of Mrs. Young, painted by New Hope artist John F. Folinsbee, was hung in the lobby on Belmont Avenue. Later, it was given a place of honor near the third-floor elevator in the north wing of West State, where it is lit by the afternoon sun that highlights the bright twinkle in her eyes. Here the nurses can see it best—an inspiration to all, as she was.

In mid-1968, Marik resigned to join a hospital consulting firm, Norman Brady Associates in Princeton, NJ, effective January 1, 1969. Bradford Jameson, assistant administrator at Bryn Mawr Hospital, replaced him. While the day-to-day operations of the hospital carried on, negotiations on the land and plans for relocation stalled in the face of this major disruption.

Renovations continued, volunteers still brought home-canned fruits and vegetables to stock the hospital's pantry, William Casterlin was named controller of the hospital and, at the request of the medical staff, all sales of tobacco were banned in the building. A consultant hired by the V.I.A. said the community could need a 167-bed hospital by 1971, 225 beds by 1980 and eventually 600 beds.

Perennial favorites Dr. Brad Green and Mrs. Pauline Young retired within five months of each other, ending an era in medicine and nursing. Dr. Gribb and Miss Cameron were named to replace them. Dr. Thomas Woodman, a Point Pleasant psychiatrist, joined the staff, bringing a new area of specialization to Doylestown Hospital.

The decade opened with more changes to the people side of the hospital. Dr. John A. Prickett retired as chief of Radiology after more than 30 years, having come to the Belmont Avenue hospital when it opened in 1939. Originally assisted by just one technician, Mrs. Lois Stone, under Dr. Prickett the department had grown to three office secretaries, four techs, five radiologists and a darkroom tech. Dr. Donald E. Parlee was elected in his place. A few months later, Mrs. Stone followed her old boss into retirement. She held the record for length of service—31 years and 6 months.

And on September 15, 1970, Brad Jameson resigned. Negotiations to bring Jerry Marik back to Doylestown Hospital were successful, and in the late fall he resumed his duties as administrator.

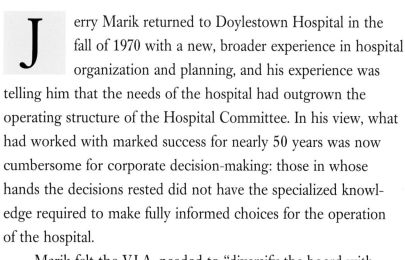

J erry Marik returned to Doylestown Hospital in the fall of 1970 with a new, broader experience in hospital organization and planning, and his experience was telling him that the needs of the hospital had outgrown the operating structure of the Hospital Committee. In his view, what had worked with marked success for nearly 50 years was now cumbersome for corporate decision-making: those in whose hands the decisions rested did not have the specialized knowledge required to make fully informed choices for the operation of the hospital.

Marik felt the V.I.A. needed to "diversify the board with community members—not as advisors, but as full board members. This was not an attempt to modify *ownership,* but to give the hospital board substantial independence to operate the hospital, taking only specific major issues to the V.I.A. for discussion and approval—like changing bylaws, taking on indebtedness or expanding the hospital." The V.I.A. would remain the owner and would continue to influence strategy.

He first advised the Hospital Committee of this view in the early '70s, and the committee's solicitor, Arthur Eastburn, appeared to concur. However, the committee did not sufficiently share Marik's concern to act on it then, and action to restructure was further postponed while land deals and relocation plans competed for everyone's attention.

Former farmland hosts simultaneous construction projects:
carving a bypass and raising a hospital.

COURTESY: INTELLIGENCER/RECORD

Shaping the future hospital

With Marik's return, the Hospital Committee rededicated its energy to determining what it should do next to meet the all-too-evident needs of a burgeoning community. Between 1960 and 1970, the borough itself exploded with more than 2,000 new residents, and surrounding populations showed similar unprecedented growth. Schools, home construction, public utilities, stores and services, highways and businesses—all were scrambling to stay on top of the trend. The community's hospital had a lot of keeping-up to do.

Negotiations resumed with Delaware Valley College. Another interested buyer had emerged, and the committee found itself bidding against a major corporation that wanted to put a gasoline and service station on the acreage the hospital was eyeing. According to Prue Suydam, who played an active part in the negotiations, Jerry Marik and friends of the hospital on the college's board of trustees pressed the hometown advantage when they learned the oil company was far outbidding the hospital. Marik met with the local college trustees and proposed that the hospital pay a reasonable sum for the land. As additional compensation, the hospital would cooperate with a strategy that strongly supported the college in its bid to reshape its image from the antique, nearly derogatory designation of "farm school." The hospital readily agreed to highlight, in every mention of its impending move, the generosity and cooperation of the board of trustees of "Delaware Valley College of Science and Agriculture"—better publicity, the rest of the trustees came to agree, than what could be provided by a sale to any oil company. It was a comfortable compromise for Prue Suydam and Jerry Marik to make to get the property that so perfectly suited the hospital's needs.

On June 29, 1971, Delaware Valley College sold two parcels

Supporting Relocation

Dr. Ed Knopf remembers "the V.I.A. ladies came right out to our offices" to discuss the move with the doctors. He estimates nearly all 86 or 87 of the physicians on staff were interviewed personally by the women.

Excerpt from a letter to the V.I.A. by Dr. A. Thomas Richie: "...I have been asked to report to you as the present secretary of the Medical Staff that following the thorough and inspiring report of progress made to the Staff by Mrs. Suydam and Mrs. Gross, the Staff voted unanimously to support the recommendation of the Hospital and hereby urge the V.I.A. to undertake this step.

"If there is any question as to 'whether a women's club should undertake such a venture,' as Mrs. Suydam remarked, our answer was best expressed by Dr. McGraw, 'From past experience, who could do better?'"

totaling 50 acres to the Village Improvement Association for $332,934. The 35-acre parcel close to Route 202 and a narrow, 15-acre piece behind it that ran north along the proposed bypass were purchased with $330,000 in unrestricted endowment funds, enabling the V.I.A. to buy the land without borrowing.

On February 10, 1972, at a special meeting of the Hospital Committee to review the final study regarding relocating or remaining on site, the committee voted unanimously to relocate. The go-ahead it sought came February 29 when the Executive Committee of the V.I.A. and the full association membership voted unanimously to build a new hospital on the former college land out West State Street at a projected cost of just under $10 million.

Meanwhile, by 1972 the hospital learned the state had allocated to it between $5 million and $7 million in a Hill-Burton guaranteed subsidized loan. This was a "pleasant surprise," according to Marik, since so many hospitals had applied. Because the hospital was required to notify the Hill-Burton program administrators by a certain date to accept or decline, the Hospital Planning Committee began working feverishly to get plans to the point where the hospital could meet with the state to satisfy the many conditions on the loan.

The planning committee, the architects and representatives from the medical and hospital staffs devised a plan for an acute short-term 165-bed hospital and accompanying services that all believed would meet the projected needs of the community and still be financially feasible.

Dorothy Kibbe, RN, who became director of nursing in September 1971, recalls her months in the old hospital as the new was taking shape. She served on 11 of the 14 committees formed by Marik to work with the architects, and remembers that Nursing was intensely involved in laying out and planning the new hospital.

"First we had to get the shape, then the location of everything, then how to make departments contiguous to make it efficient," she says. "The 14 committees were responsible for setting up the new systems."

On Belmont Avenue, only the supply room was centralized. Kibbe's contribution to the new design, which she adapted from Sacred Heart Hospital in Norristown, was to modernize the management of materials into SPD, or Supplies/Processing/Distribution. Mail, flowers, food, equipment and drugs are delivered to a back entrance where they are processed, then distributed on carts to the various areas.

Bill Casterlin, assistant administrator, digs in at the groundbreaking September 16, 1973.

But the greatest system change, perhaps, from Belmont Avenue to West State Street was that nearly every function expanded from one room to an entire department. One obvious example was the Emergency Room. In 1970, doctors and anesthetists still had to be called from home after 9 p.m. when needed. The new facility would have a full-time, fully staffed Emergency *Department*.

Fundraising and building on a grand scale

On September 16, 1973, ground was broken in former cow pastures under beautiful autumn skies that augured well for the building project.

The Capital Fund Planning Committee of the V.I.A. was established with community, medical staff, V.I.A. and Hospital Committee representation. Prue Suydam had been appointed chair of the Relocation Fund Drive at the close of her term as Hospital Committee chair in 1972. Nancy Perry replaced her as head of the Hospital Committee at this critical time in the hospital's history.

The Special Gifts Campaign, chaired by Carolyn Taylor and aimed toward all volunteers, the V.I.A. and the Junior Woman's Club, netted $225,000—an impressive $75,000 more than its goal. James A. Michener again gave his name and time to the hospital's effort, speaking at the dinner for the last phase of the Relocation Fund Drive when the Community Fund Drive kicked off in February 1974.

In May, the tally came in: the relocation appeal brought in $1,571,665, with every campaign division oversubscribing its goal. And in recognition of her remarkable efforts on behalf of the hospital, Prue Suydam was honored with the Benjamin Rush Award of the Bucks County Medical Society and a Central Bucks Chamber of Commerce Distinguished Service Award.

Nancy Perry, Jane Sienkiewicz and Prue Suydam, current and former Hospital Committee chairs, dig in and make hospital history at the groundbreaking ceremony in September 1973.

"Dr. Gribb was young and brought new ideas. Dr. Green, who took him under his wing, would say 'Now, John...' and hold him back to a degree. But eventually, the new ideas became more and more popular." Dr. Gribb characterized this as involving the family as a group, "instead of just taking your body and delivering it of the baby."

—Betty Murray,
    staff nurse 1959–1966,
    nurse manager 1966–1990

Hospital Figures
FY70–71

5,658	Adult and pediatric patients
834	Births
3,099	Surgical procedures
25,148	Radiological procedures
93,851	Lab procedures
1,726	Physical therapy procedures
3,986	EKGs
9,168	Emergency procedures
5,014	VN-HC visits
6.7 days	Average length of stay, adult and pediatric
89.3%	Average med-surg occupancy

Transitions

W hile the Hospital Committee and its contractors were giving birth out on West State to a new facility, back on Belmont Avenue the hospital and its staff were giving birth as well.

Since 1968, maternity services instituted major—and, some believed, long overdue—changes, as fathers began to be permitted into labor and delivery areas at the urging of progressive GPs and their patients. By 1970 Dr. Gribb, believing that husbands would just be a hindrance if they didn't know what was going on, encouraged the nurses' foray into prenatal classes. Says Betty Murray, RN, ob/gyn nurse manager from 1966 to 1990, "We had to practice in front of Dr. Gribb to get approval for how we would present the prenatal classes to the people. He was a great foreseer of what could happen—he insisted we plan it and be ready so it flowed smoothly."

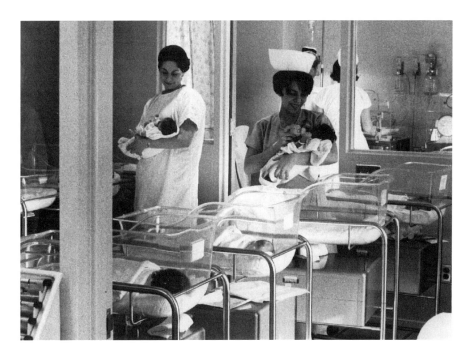

Betty Murray, RN, and Karen Bender in the nursery, 1970   DOYLESTOWN HOSPITAL ARCHIVES

On January 14, 1971, the first class was held in the auditorium of the James Lorah Memorial Home. Husbands who wanted to accompany their wives in labor and delivery *had* to take the course. "By the end, the husbands were more into it than some of the wives," Murray remembers. The class sessions were held over five weeks and topics included human reproduction, a medical examination, prenatal care, labor and delivery, baby care and a tour of the hospital's facilities. The course was not limited to Doylestown Hospital's patients—patients planning to use other hospitals would take it because so few such programs were available as yet. And the program grew and grew.

By June 1973, Murray had lobbied for more upgrades to the "care" of maternity patients' families. Beginning on Father's Day, visiting hours in Maternity changed, ending at 8 p.m. instead of 8:30—for everyone but the new fathers. They could stay on until 8:45 and, in mask and gown, hold their newborns, visit as a family with their wives and receive some instruction on baby care from the nursing staff.

A year later, family-oriented obstetrical care took another leap: newborns were permitted to stay in the room with their mothers as long as Mom wished, and Dad could visit and hold his baby from 12:30 to 8:45 p.m.

Dorothy Kibbe was particularly sensitive to the general transition in nursing in the early '70s.

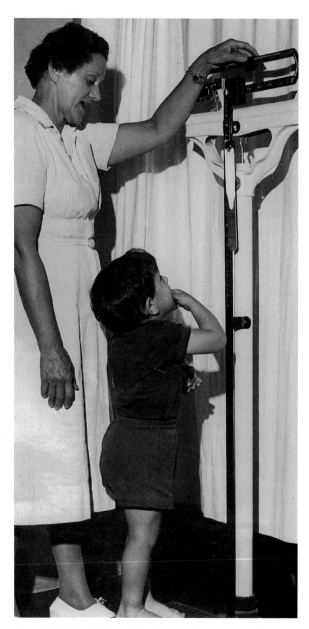

Mrs. Adelaide McLaughlin, RN, and a young patient
DOYLESTOWN HOSPITAL ARCHIVES

122

Involving the nursing staff in the design of the new building accentuated the changing role of the nurse in patient care, allowing nurses to more readily cast off what she refers to as "the Florence Nightingale role." More education led to greater clinical understanding—and that created a new kind of nurse in health care.

"My tenure was a troubled time," Kibbe says. "Until then, nurses were the handmaidens of the doctors. I struggled with the nursing staff to teach them that they have to think for themselves.

"I fought for the nurses," she says. "I felt I was their advocate. It was important to me that they be prepared for a profession, not just training for a job. Maybe I moved some little stones—it was the job of others to move the big boulders."

Nothing stands still

The administration, staff and Hospital Committee struggled through this time, dually focused on both the new hospital going up in stages and the current building that still housed all the health care so vital to the community. Advances in patient care were not put on hold until the new site could be occupied. In March 1971, work began on the Critical Care Unit that would contain two coronary care beds and two intensive care beds when it opened a few months later. As the Belmont building became progressively more crowded, the Hospital Committee renovated the Darlington house on Maple Avenue in 1971 to accommodate Visiting Nurse-Home Care. The Short Procedure Unit, now called Same-Day Services, opened mornings on Belmont in November 1974 in Pediatrics. Patients were prepped and operated on the same day, putting the hospital ahead of the times.

People moved into new jobs, reflecting the changing face of administering this growing facility and hinting at the huge complexity

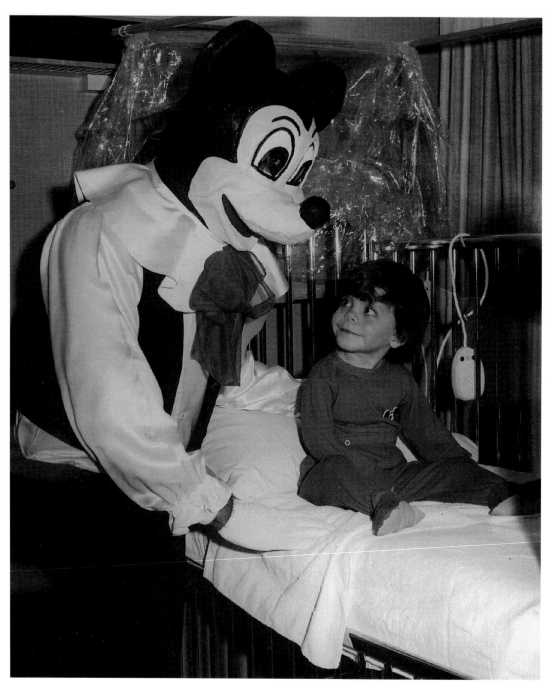

Big-name star visits Pediatrics.

DOYLESTOWN HOSPITAL ARCHIVES

that was just around the corner. When Nancy Perry was named chair of the Hospital Committee, she relinquished her post as the first paid director of volunteers. The Hospital Committee hired Anne Funk to succeed her, continuing its commitment to a well-organized and -maintained volunteer force. Bill Casterlin was named assistant administrator in fall 1972, making way for Jim Brownlow to take over as controller.

In February 1975, the hospital honored 97 full- and part-timers for 5-to-25 years of service to Doylestown Hospital during the first employee service awards, and the hospital noted that 301 adult volunteers, including seven men, had given 26,141 hours in the last year.

In September, the hospital established a school of radiology, which would open its doors in the new building with Charles F. McCleary, RT, as director of education for the two-year course. This program ran successfully for more than 20 years before changes in the healthcare industry made it advisable to phase it out and allow college programs to fill the need.

125

Doylestown Hospital, circa 1975

126

Commemorative tile given to participants in Moving Day, November 15, 1975

Welcome home

J ust when it seemed there would forever be a pall of construction dust hovering over the old cow pasture next to Lenape Junior High, the crews began to move out and the equipment moved in. There were still sections inside left incomplete, awaiting the next stage in the building's story. But the departments, so delightfully fresh and new, stood ready for their occupants—staff and patients—and the chatter and clatter that make a hospital come alive.

On November 2, 1975, Bob Cathcart, now president of the American Hospital Association, spoke at the dedication of this $12.6 million, 200,000-square-foot, 165-bed hospital on West State Street. The third Doylestown Hospital was ideally situated with plenty of parking (no more doctors' cars in neighbors' back yards), room for future expansion

127

(they were already planning) and easy access to major highways (you couldn't miss it).

Moving Day, November 15, was an unforgettable display of community involvement, careful planning and incredibly good fortune. The sun shone on the parade of the decade as 65 patients were moved by staff, administration and volunteers in 22 Bucks County and New Jersey ambulances.

Marik remembers the hard work that went into preparing for the move. Although all departments planned for the relocation, according to their functions, "Nursing was the key department planning

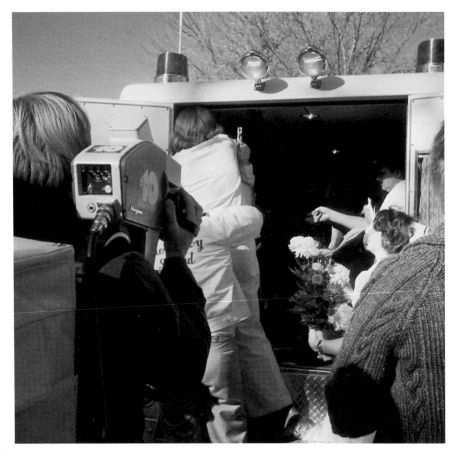

Television crews were on hand to record the cooperative community effort.
DOYLESTOWN HOSPITAL ARCHIVES

Cavalcade of ambulances, November 15, 1975

for the moving of the hospital's patients. Our first consideration was that whatever care the patients needed, they'd get."

"The move, which was expected to take four hours, was completed in just over two," Dorothy Kibbe proudly reports. "We discharged a lot of patients, keeping only those needing acute care. I rented a motorhome and set it up at the old emergency room and worked out of that for about 40 hours. I made a big pot of vegetable soup to keep in the motorhome—we worked through the night before we moved.

"At the time, the area had about 16 ambulance companies competing for each other's business," she says. "Months ahead of time, I met with the different crews to coordinate the transport of the patients.

They squabbled at first, but finally settled in of their own accord. The ambulances lined up the night before. We had one crew that had life support equipment and they stood by in case we had an emergency. It was a beautiful sight to see the response from the utilities and service organizations."

It was necessary to set up guidelines, plan the order of transport, work with police to establish the traffic patterns and close off the streets, staff both sites the day of the move, and then decide when to shut down the operating and emergency rooms. And they rehearsed.

"Things went so well," says Marik, "we were done around 11:30 a.m. We'd anticipated all kinds of problems," but none materialized.

Flynn Edwards was the patient most remember, so flamboyant was he. An artist involved with the Broadway stage, he had a way of

Reflecting on Relocation

Judy Melson, former V.I.A. president and Hospital Board chair, about the move to West State Street: "It was very hard to say to those people who had contributed for all those years, 'This is the building we're now going to abandon, and we're going to start all over. So, basically, everything you've given us to this point will be—Gone!' We'd just added a new wing in 1965!

"At the time, that was when third-party reimbursement was entirely different than it is now. We're talking about everything, costs plus. Blue Cross was our major funding source. Third-party payers were paying for everything it cost to run your hospital plus anything you wanted to build. So there was no thought to curtailing your space. That was the mentality that we had when we moved to the site. Then when we got to the site, third-party reimbursement completely reversed in 15 years. A new story. But for what we did at that time, it was certainly the right choice. It's a blessing it happened in the financial environment it did.

"A lot of towns are coping with satellite services, and to have it all on one campus is the beauty of it here."

attracting attention even in the midst of such high drama as the parade of ambulances along State Street through Doylestown. The last to go, he rode out wrapped in a big fur coat and almost hidden beneath a huge bouquet of roses.

With far less fanfare, Mrs. J. Kent Smith entered the record books by making her way from old to new hospital in active labor. She delivered West State's first baby—Peter K. Smith—at 11:05 a.m. in the new emergency department and quietly—or perhaps not *so* quietly— reminded everyone what this was *really* about.

*Hundreds attended the open house for
the new hospital, November 2, 1975.*

DOYLESTOWN HOSPITAL ARCHIVES

133

With the move to its new quarters in 1975, Doylestown Hospital entered a period of profound inner growth and change, even as it reached out to the wider community to develop partnerships, deliver enhanced services and bring more medical professionals and nonmedical employees on staff.

While the population of the borough remained stable at 8,500, that of the surrounding Doylestown Township grew from 6,600 in 1970 to 11,800 in 1980 and 14,500 in 1990. Residential development rapidly filled farmland, while the people in those new homes filled the schools and highways. Expatriate residents returning for visits don't recognize their old haunts—they tend to get disoriented when they head out of town on once familiar, once "country" roads.

Ginnie Sommerer and Lucinda Harrold in the Gift Shop, April 1978. The shop bears a plaque honoring Lucinda and Kathryn Miller, long-time volunteers.

COURTESY: GIAN LUISO, *INTELLIGENCER/RECORD*

In a decade and a half, Doylestown Hospital's budget swelled from $8,378,975 to $52,125,650—an astronomical increase, especially when compared to $4.6 million in 1973–74 at Belmont Avenue. But the services the hospital added kept pace not only with the increased population; they met the needs of the changing face of insurance provisions and the economy, advances in medicine and technology and the higher expectations of a better informed healthcare consumer.

When members of the V.I.A., the Hospital Committee and the administration stepped through the doors of the new hospital, they passed through much more than a couple of slabs of glass. The commitment they made to the community was tested more, here on West State, than it ever had been in the comparatively simple times that were now behind them, part of their "adolescence," part of their history.

Partnering to keep patients in the community

Original community surveys in the early '70s had determined that one of the area's leading healthcare needs was for in-patient psychiatric services so people who needed treatment could remain in the community and not be sent to the state hospital. In response to this need, mental health services had been established in 1975 as a crisis unit of the emergency department at Belmont Avenue. When the Hospital Planning Committee laid out the new facility, plans had included space for a mental health unit on the top floor, but state approval failed to come through in time for the construction. However, anticipating the eventual go-ahead, the area was shelled and blocked off.

According to Dr. Edwin Knopf, director of the Lenape Valley Foundation for Mental Health in Chalfont at the time, the hospital and Lenape Valley negotiated a plan in the mid-'70s calling for its mental health outpatient services to move to the hospital grounds in a separate

Ruth Toner, chair of the planning committee, and Jaromir Marik examine plans for the psychiatric unit that opened on the top floor in 1978.

building. But when community resistance arose to the idea of a mental health "hospital" as a neighbor, the plan to build a separate outpatient unit was withdrawn.

The hospital opened its 18-bed mental health unit in the shelled area (later designated 4East, Behavioral Health Unit) on June 15, 1978, at a final cost of $316,609—$48,000 under budget—bringing the hospital's total bed count to 183. Lenape Valley's staff psychiatrists supported the hospital staff.

In 1982, when Dr. Knopf became the first medical director for Doylestown Hospital, Lenape Valley and the hospital dusted off and updated their old partnership plans for putting an outpatient facility on the grounds. "The pulse of the community we served had changed; the timing was better. Instead of pushing at it from the outside," he says of the proposal, "we pulled at it from the inside."

Another CAT Tale
Doylestown Hospital began sharing the services of the mobile CAT scanner with Grand View and Warminster General Hospitals in 1979.

Any Connection?
In January 1979 the first full-time chaplain, the Rev. Roy Bucher of Doylestown Mennonite Church, came on board. That year, the hospital snack bar was granted approval to open on Sundays.

The hospital undertook the planning, approvals, financing and construction for the outpatient facility on its grounds, with Lenape Valley Foundation as lessee. In 1985, LVF opened its separate, not-for-profit mental health facility with administrative offices and an outpatient therapy unit along the new access road toward West Street.

As this project was underway, Doylestown Hospital was also working with Penn Foundation for Mental Health in Sellersville and Grand View, North Penn and Quakertown Community Hospitals to build a 50-bed psychiatric hospital in Sellersville. In 1984, this grand "Psychiatric Joint Venture" failed in mid-planning when reviews at state and local levels determined that the five-county area had sufficient beds for mental health patients. Confronted with that verdict, the group withdrew its application for the psychiatric hospital.

Signs of the times as the decade closes

The V.I.A. had hosted its first Designer House in 1971, bringing in local firms to renovate the old farmstead at Wheelbarrow Hill in Holicong. Though a successful venture, it was another five years before the women tried it again. Their second Designer House was the V.I.A.'s own Darlington House, which had been abandoned by the VN-HC service, and the effort brought $6,566 to the hospital fund in 1976. For many years, all Designer House proceeds went to the hospital. In recent years, however, the V.I.A. has chosen to share with other programs about a quarter of what the popular event realizes every spring. The 1997 Designer House made more than $94,000.

In this period, the hospital began accepting Bank Americard and MasterCharge for payments and established a Speakers Bureau as a community source of professional viewpoints and presentations. The Hospital Committee revised the chair's term to four years and the

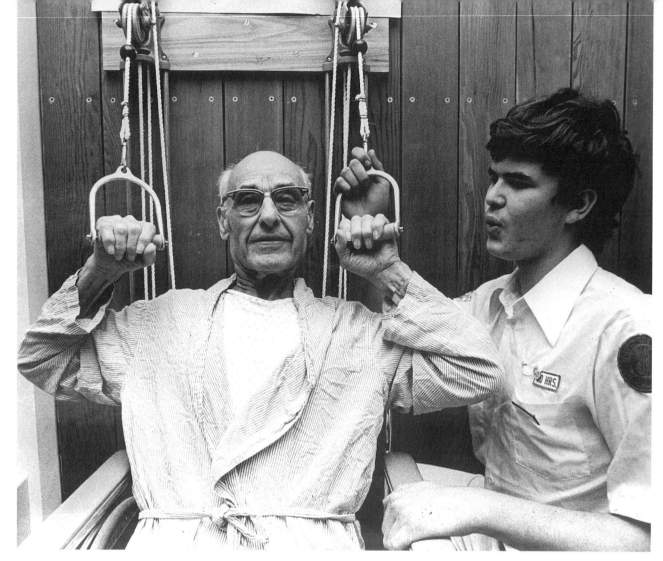

Teen volunteer Edward Honer works with patient Charles Wiedmann, May 5, 1978.

vice chairs' to two, and it formed a committee to determine what medical staff specialties were required to grow in response to the community's needs. The hospital had developed to the point that surely none of its founders would recognize it. For example, the 1978–79 budget was $12.2 million, 595 active volunteers gave 60,370 hours, and 610 full- and part-time employees were working with people and maintaining the services and facility.

Nursing Staff Development

The nursing department paralleled the development in doctors' specialties, remembers Marge Franklin, RN, who came to Doylestown Hospital in 1955 as a part-time night nurse making $10 to $12 a shift. "As each part of health care advanced in technology, the nursing department advanced also." It came a long way from "pills and injections." For example, Dr. McGarvey began teaching classes to nurses who needed more education to care for patients in the new four-bed ICU (intensive care unit) at Belmont in 1967.

The standard nurse's uniform Franklin and so many other nurses knew— white stockings, white shoes, white dress and caps identifying the different nursing programs—"went by the wayside." In the '70s, the women were granted permission to wear pantsuits. When infection control rules were instituted, and operating room nurses began changing into scrubs, most nurses also opted to wear scrubs at work. By the mid-'80s, nurses in different departments wanted "an identity," giving rise to the practice of wearing "uniform" casual outfits. But according to Marge Franklin, what the long-departed nursing caps symbolized is still there: professionalism, education, dedication. "They're still on their heads."

She recalls that nurses were expected to stand up—no matter what—"and give a doctor your seat when he came into the room." She quickly points out: "We didn't take that to the new hospital."

Franklin became the first vice president of nursing in 1977, two years after the move to West State Street. "We started the position of a sort of staff coordinator, who set up a pattern for permanent staffing of all nursing positions within the department. We also developed 'head nurses' into 'managers' responsible for interviewing, hiring recommendations, performance evaluations, developing budgets for areas."

The Nursing Education Department developed at the beginning of the '80s, and patient education grew alongside it through the '80s with such programs as the cardiac rehab nurse, ostomy patient care coordinator, infection control nurse and diabetic patient educator. It added a new dimension to the nursing department, which was expanding rapidly when Franklin retired in 1987.

According to Franklin, when Dorothy Kibbe, director of nursing 1969–77, drew the organizational chart, she "had the insight" to reverse it and put the community and the patient at the top where the CEO had been. "I think that's how the hospital evolved—it expected to meet the community's needs."

In March 1979, Doylestown Borough Council created the Doylestown Hospital Bond Authority, enabling the hospital to sell tax-exempt bonds and buy back its mortgage. The Mortgage Modification Plan, completed in July 1979, was technically an interest-rate modification, not a refinancing, and it saved the hospital $1.6 million over the remaining 19 years of the mortgage.

Bringing the decade to a successful finish and making a handy start on the '80s, Doylestown Hospital won for the V.I.A. the top prize in the national Community Improvement Program sponsored by the General Federation of Women's Clubs and Sears Roebuck Foundation, beating out 11,000 other entries for a prize of $10,000 and a large, inscribed sterling tray. Mrs. Leroy W. (Vera) Shutt, Hospital Committee chair, prepared a scrapbook and narrative about the hospital for the entry, which also took first place at the state and regional levels to qualify for final competition at the GFWC Convention in St. Louis, MO, in June 1980.

A Candy Striper—teenaged volunteer—talks to a patient.
DOYLESTOWN HOSPITAL ARCHIVES

The judges' praise surely validated V.I.A. members and warmed their hearts: "This project stands above all others because it has a long history of community service, [and] it anticipates the future needs of the community. It is a project which from its inception has moved beyond what has traditionally been expected of a woman. It also is a project which serves the rich as well as the poor with grace and dignity."

Plans for the long term

The new long-range plan for the hospital included its response to the need for local rehabilitation services. According to Jerry Marik, Doylestown Hospital was the first general community hospital in Bucks County and the Philadelphia area to receive approval on its application from the Comprehensive Health Planning Agency to build a physical rehabilitation center. By December 1980, plans were finalized to construct and equip a comprehensive rehab center to include inpatient and outpatient physical and occupational services, speech therapy and, most important, a 30-bed inpatient

The Tradition of Service

Pat Berry, current chair of the Hospital Board, laughs good-naturedly about being recruited for the V.I.A. Hospital Committee in the mid-'80s, before restructuring: "I was told, when I first came on the board, 'This'll only take about two hours.' They *lied! Big time* they lied! The very first meeting, we sat there over four hours—[at that time] all the reports were given orally. That was a real eye-opener."

Liz Westcott estimates that often she and her fellow Hospital Committee members would each put in about 60 hours a week, with all the meetings and volunteer hours. "You never got away with less than 40 hours a week."

Ruth Schleicher, V.I.A. president 1988–90, notes that both her mother and mother-in-law were active members. She grew up with the V.I.A. and the hospital—as did many local women who are involved today. As a volunteer in high school, she helped prepare the trays after school under the watchful eye of Mrs. Cramer, who was in charge of the kitchen.

The women of the V.I.A. are universally proud of their work for the hospital. Despite long hours, juggling family responsibilities and recruiting husbands and children to help out, not a one who was interviewed would trade those years and miss out on the camaraderie, the successes or the unmatched rewards of giving of themselves to something as vital as this community hospital.

rehab unit. With other support and ancillary services, the cost was a staggering $8.6 million. Approved modifications to Radiology and the gift shop storage area added another $98,000 to the ticket price.

"Progress In Care/81" was the three-year fundraising venture undertaken by the Hospital Committee to finance these projects. Kicked off with the $10,000 GFWC-Sears prize awarded to the V.I.A., it far exceeded its goal of $450,000 by the formal end of the pledge period in October 1981. Bonds were sold for $100 each, giving many the chance to own a piece of the hospital.

The Hospital Committee broke ground for the rehab unit, "Wing C," on December 6, opened it in March 1983, and dedicated it in early June. Progress In Care/81 reached its final year with a total of $821,421.

In the rest of the hospital, the day-to-day advances continued. Celebratory champagne dinners were offered to new parents for the first time in November 1981, and Maternity initiated one-day sibling education classes. Dr. Charles Burmeister, a Plumsteadville family practitioner, became the first member of the medical staff on the Hospital Committee in 1981–82, when the Joint Commission on Accreditation of Hospitals recommended such a step to the committee. He was termed a "Medical Staff

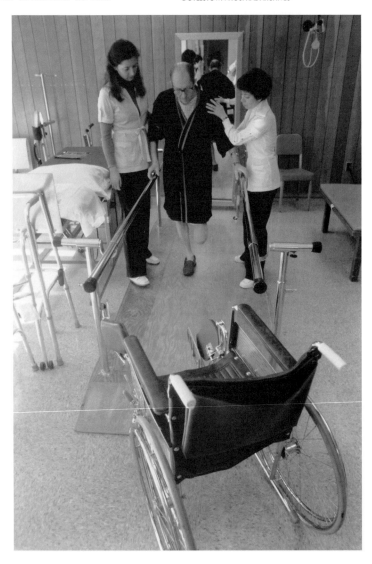

Kathy Reilly, PT aide, and Terri McCarthy, LPT, assist Mr. Hager in Physical Therapy, 1982.

DOYLESTOWN HOSPITAL ARCHIVES

A Bridge Across Eras

Jim Brownlow, the hospital's COO, has the unique experience of bridging both administrations and the attendant changes in leadership and philosophy—in fact, creating and facilitating, in many ways, that bridge across the years since 1972 when he joined the hospital administration as controller. Both Jerry Marik and Rich Reif genuinely respect his abilities and dedication, and they honor the great difference he has made at Doylestown Hospital.

"He brought credibility to both eras," says Reif. "He neither destroyed the past nor glamorizes the present—he is the reality."

Jim is the person with the answers to *how* the hospital works because he carries out, behind-the-scenes, the overall vision—quietly, competently and with humor. As the only administrator who has worked with both the former Hospital Committee and the current board structure—and with two distinctly different administrations under Jerry Marik and Rich Reif—it is clear that Jim adheres tenaciously to what

he terms "the firm, visible legacy of the V.I.A." With a spark of his gentle humor, he bows to the V.I.A.'s authority: "My assistant is a V.I.A. member, so technically I work for her—and periodically she reminds me of that."

Jim recalls an ice storm in the mid-'80s that knocked out the hospital's electric power. The hospital had a "full house," emergency generators couldn't operate the heating systems and the temperature was dropping fast. The electric company—PECO—quickly weighed the options and determined the only choice it had was to divert power temporarily from local residences and businesses to the hospital until full repairs could be made. "Even so, it took three hours to get the temperature up," he says, recalling his concern for the patients. He also readily acknowledges the community's sacrifice that day, and those made by others in similar emergencies: staff and volunteers extending their shifts, remaining overnight to fill in when needed. These stories still warm him years later.

Hospice Program

"My dealing with death and dying [as medical director at the Neshaminy Manor nursing home and with cancer patients] prepared me for allowing people to die a natural death at home...keeping people comfortable rather than putting them through what we [often] put them through today.

"I was doing hospice before hospice was Hospice, taking care of terminally ill patients at home, as many doctors do. I'd sort of fallen into it. My wife and I went around and talked to women's clubs and groups of people...about cancer and heart disease, and that led into talking about end-of-life decisions, how to deal with this and how to treat it.

"Before 1940, everyone went to the home and held hands, and people died at home. People knew how to handle this. They don't now, and so they need help to do it right. We go pretty close to the bone, but we stop short of euthanasia:...make them comfortable, relieve pain.

"Part of hospice is the ministerial and spiritual aspect of death and dying, [which involves] doctors, nurses, a minister and the volunteers.

"I think it's done a helluva job. I'm very proud of it. It's an area I believe in, in terms of my friends and my family and my patients."

—interview, Richard R. Vanderbeek, MD,
former medical director of Hospice

Consultant to the V.I.A." and had no voting rights. These were still reserved for V.I.A. members alone.

The Hospice Program developed over 1982–83, with Dr. Richard R. Vanderbeek as medical director, but not until 1987 was it evaluated for the first time—becoming the third hospice program in the state to receive JCAH accreditation. Now one branch of the hospital's Visiting Nurse-Home Care Department, Hospice is supported by medical insurance payments and donations, and is staffed by visiting nurses, physicians and volunteers. The program provides patients in the final stage of their illnesses whatever medications or nursing and physician care they need, as well as training, emotional support and bereavement counseling for their loved ones.

Sarabond, How Could You Do This to Me?

It could be a country-western song about love and betrayal. Instead, it's the name of a mortar additive made by the Dow Chemical Company and used in the prefabricated brick panels of the 1975 building (now the North Wing). In July 1983, the hospital learned that Sarabond may cause chemical reactions that corrode the steel connecting bolts and lifting rods embedded in the panels. This would lead to masonry deterioration—and, quite possibly, chunks of the façade breaking away and falling to the ground. In January 1986 the hospital filed suit against Dow and others, seeking reimbursement of its costs and other damages. In 1988, the hospital began an extensive $10 million restoration in which it removed and replaced the entire brick façade of the original building. When all was done, the hospital had a new face, a settlement for an undisclosed sum from Dow—and a handsome clip of a front-page *Wall Street Journal* article datelined "Doylestown, Pa."

In 1982, the hospital bought the 6.7-acre Raymond McGregor estate, a piece of unimproved land at Shady Retreat Road and West Street contiguous to the hospital's original 50 acres. This allowed the hospital to build a second entrance, which also serves Lenape Valley Foundation.

Restructuring

I n July 1984, the hospital implemented the federally mandated Prospective Pricing System based on diagnostic related groups (DRGs). This huge shift in how third-party reimbursement was handled dramatically affected the operation of the hospital and led to increasing VN-HC visits and demand for hospice care as healthcare systems and patients sought new ways to provide and receive services.

Pat Meier, RN, with preschoolers at "Hello Hospital" program, 1982

DOYLESTOWN HOSPITAL ARCHIVES

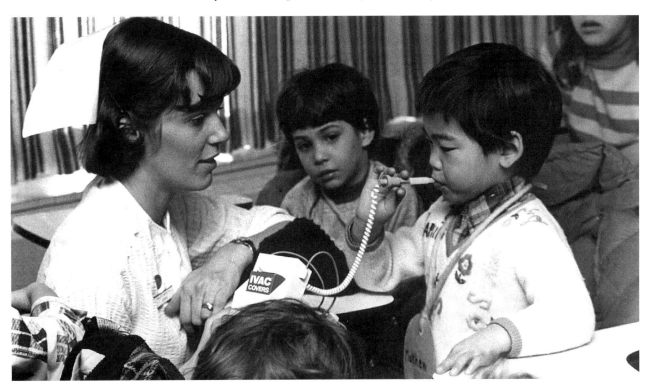

Struggling with these events and other financial issues emphasized to the V.I.A. and the Hospital Committee the need for corporate restructuring. Marik updated his recommendations from the '70s and came up with this set of reasons to examine fully the current structure of the two organizations:

- Legal—Litigation and other legalities make a change in structure imperative.
- Diversification—With third-party reimbursements declining and hospitals looking for new forms of income, separate corporations are needed to avoid endangering the hospital's not-for-profit healthcare status.
- Financial—To protect V.I.A. assets and have more avenues for investment, both the hospital and the V.I.A. need to change their structures.
- Governance—The Hospital Committee needs greater diversity in its voting membership and to operate more independently of the V.I.A. to speed its decision-making.

An ad hoc committee appointed by the V.I.A. in summer 1984 examined the existing corporate structure. The outstanding characteristic was that the hospital was not a legal entity—only the V.I.A. was incorporated—so everything the hospital did potentially put the V.I.A., its membership and its assets at risk. The Hospital Committee engaged Dechert Price & Rhoads (DPR) of Philadelphia, a legal firm with a strong hospital background, with which it developed recommendations for reorganization. Bill Humenuk at DPR, in charge of the hospital division, was "bright, friendly, honest and knowledgeable," Marik recalls. From their discussions came recommendations to create the V.I.A. Health System. The plan gained V.I.A. approval in November 1985 and became effective March 1, 1986.

Signs of Growth
In 1983, the hospital had 942 full- and part-time employees, 150 on its medical staff and 935 volunteers giving 77,765 hours.

Service to Community
In 1984–85, the Free Care Committee of the hospital helped pay bills for 283 patients for a total of $54,097 in general free care, VN-HC, maternity and hospice care.

V.I.A. president Judy Melson during negotiations to restructure the Hospital Committee and the V.I.A.

DOYLESTOWN HOSPITAL ARCHIVES

With the new year, corporate restructuring dissolved the 63-year-old Hospital Committee and established the V.I.A. Health System of four distinct corporations with separate boards of directors for each: Doylestown Hospital, Doylestown Health Foundation to hold funds and investments, V.I.A. Affiliates to organize profit or not-for-profit ventures, and the Village Improvement Association over all. V.I.A. members chair and hold the majority on all boards and the V.I.A. retains ownership of each corporation.

Judy Melson, president of the V.I.A. from 1984 to 1986, recalls the process of restructuring. "We didn't want to give up what the women had fought for for 90 years, but we also didn't want to be tied to cumbersome methods. It was hard to do that, hard to give up. But the V.I.A. graciously did so. They certainly put their trust in Jerry Marik. There was never any friction on *what* was to be done."

147

For the hospital, this meant transitions. As last chair of the Hospital Committee and first chair of the Hospital Board, Betty Nunemaker served the last three months of her term under the new structure. For the first time, the hospital brought non-V.I.A. members with full voting privileges onto its board to create diversity in the decision-making process: the board would now include V.I.A. members, hospital administrators, medical staff and others from the community. The corporate structure provided the hospital with legal and fiscal advantages and more flexibility to pursue new services and opportunities.

A class of G.E.M.S.—Good Emergency Mother Substitutes, a babysitters course—from 1985

The first wing of Children's Village under construction, November 1984
DOYLESTOWN HOSPITAL ARCHIVES

An era of change

I n the midst of this corporate upheaval, the hospital operated as it always had, driven forward by advances in medical technology and the needs of the people it served, sometimes with drama and daring.

"Daring" certainly was in the minds of some of those who watched as, in January 1985, the hospital dedicated Children's Village, a daycare center for employees' children. One skeptic was heard to say, "Well, we can always use the space" if the project didn't work out, but that opportunity never arose. Children's Village was a success from the beginning. The facility on the hospital grounds accommodated 60 children at the outset, ages 6 weeks to 5 years, all day and

Is God a Doctor?

"The generations of family doctors who first came to this hospital were the gods of their profession. That's a difficult transition for physicians to make—to come from the level of god to 'captain of the ship' to 'quarterback of the team.' That's quite a ways to come. It's very complicated now. Some of the docs say they get really nervous about being the captain of the ship, and I tell them, 'The reason you're really nervous is because you're NOT captain of the ship! There is no ship—there's a big playing field out there.'

"I don't think docs get god fixes any more. The pendulum has swung the other way, without an *evolution*—it's been more like a *revolution*. What's happened is that the doctor says something and the patient defies that. The medical journals now are not the *New England Journal of Medicine*, but the *Ladies Home Journal*. There are some very sophisticated articles—the level of education available to the average American is phenomenal. What we worry about is how accurate and complete the information is for those readers. So the physician's challenge is greater. The doc has to pull all that information together."

—*interview, Edwin R. Knopf, MD,*
VP-Medical Support Services

The Community Health Alliance

In 1988, Doylestown Hospital and Abington Memorial Hospital formed TCHA as a vehicle to reduce costs and provide more services. Among its more concrete accomplishments were the joint purchase of the hospitals' telephone equipment and the ability to join national purchasing groups—both providing significant savings.

More subtle benefits of the alliance derive from the mere fact of its formation and continued existence. The pact between the two hospitals frees each to focus on their core competencies and their own service areas, while TCHA has shown Doylestown Hospital how it can work together with other hospitals for mutual benefit.

First of 1987

Michael Hopkins, left, son of Jennifer and Michael Hopkins of Chalfont, was born at 12:31 p.m. Brittany Wister, born at 7:53 a.m., is the daughter of Carolyn and W. Wynne Wister, Doylestown.

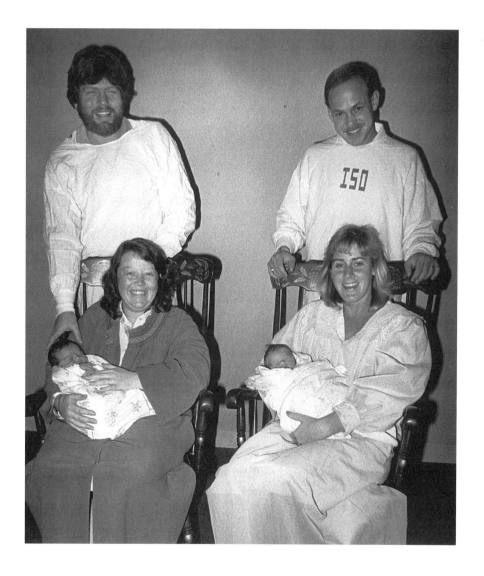

after school for elementary ages. It operated 52 weeks a year and closed only on weekends and for the handful of holidays observed by the hospital. It would expand twice over the next seven years in response to its growing reputation and the hospital's growing staff, and later open its doors to the public. It added a state-licensed, full-day kindergarten in 1986 and its summer Friendship Camp in 1990. The first nationally accredited center in Pennsylvania, it recently received its thirteenth straight accreditation "with zero deficiencies." Today, the program serves as a model for daycare centers across the region. Patsy Clayton, who piloted Children's Village since its beginning, retired in 1998 to allow, as she sees it, a director with greater experience to take the center into the future and make it more available as a learning laboratory for other organizations who aspire to bring daycare to their employees' families.

In 1986, the hospital began planning a major expansion project that would provide a new main wing to house all outpatient services and enlarge and improve more than 18 departments.

Then, in 1988, Jaromir Marik, Doylestown Hospital's first administrator, first chief executive officer and first president, announced plans to retire. His main regret was that he would not take the new wing—which he'd seen through planning, financing and contracting— through construction, opening and full operation. But that would take another five years and he'd be 70 years old. He submitted his resignation to give the board adequate time to find a successor who could work with the women of the hospital board and fit into the unique character of this little community hospital with its big healthcare-center attributes to which he'd devoted nearly 30 years.

An involved search process ensued, focusing on a final candidate who eventually was dropped from consideration when the board and the candidate could not agree to contract terms. A second search resulted in the hiring of an administrator with background in a variety of hospitals in Pennsylvania and Maryland. Richard A. Reif became Doylestown Hospital's second president and CEO on June 1, 1989.

Less than two months later, on July 25, Rich Reif presided at the groundbreaking for the new wing.

Jaromir Marik

Jerry Marik was born in Czechoslovakia. He earned his bachelor's degree in commerce and business administration from the University of British Columbia, Vancouver, in 1955 and a master's degree there in 1956. He was assistant administrator of Vancouver General Hospital, Kaiser Foundation Hospital in San Francisco and finally, Pennsylvania Hospital in Philadelphia before coming to Doylestown Hospital in 1960.

He served simultaneously as administrator of Neshaminy Manor from May 1965 to December 31, 1966, overseeing the final stages of construction of a new large building, then equipping it and getting it approved by the Joint Commission on Accreditation of Hospitals as the first nursing care facility in Pennsylvania to be so accredited.

In January 1969, Marik left Doylestown Hospital to accept a position with Norman Brady and Associates, a healthcare consulting firm, and then with Extendicare, which later became the hospital giant Humana. At the request of the Hospital Committee, Marik returned to Doylestown Hospital in November 1970.

Upon his retirement June 30, 1989, Marik was asked to serve the Hospital Board for one year as consultant on board policy matters. An agreement was drawn up to give shape to that arrangement, and Marik completed several projects initiated in cooperation with Mrs. Judy Melson, Hospital Board president.

Among the major accomplishments during his tenure as administrator are acquisition of the Delaware Valley College land in 1971, construction of the 165-bed hospital on West State Street in 1975 and V.I.A. and hospital corporate restructuring in the mid-'80s.

Marik would most like to be remembered for "the

DOYLESTOWN HOSPITAL ARCHIVES

end result: some 20,000 birth certificates with my name on them as hospital administrator, all the thousands of people treated in the Emergency Department and as inpatients and outpatients, that [the hospital] was integrated into the community life. It was an institution providing first-class care through all the years [I was there] and developed into one of the finest hospitals of its size in the Philadelphia area. And although I played a part in it and am proud of that, the hospital is too complex to say 'I did it.' I was just a part of the team that made it possible.

"When I remember the hospital as it was in those early years, I think I was really fortunate to experience it and grow with it."

Jerry Marik lives with his wife, Kay, a nurse, on a farm in Upper Makefield Township. His three daughters—Brenda, Linda and Susan—are all nurses.

153

CHAPTER 7

MORE THAN A HOSPITAL 1989–1998

J ust as the citizens of a century ago would probably disagree with a label of "sleepy" for the Doylestown of their time, neither would the citizens of this decade be fully willing to describe their town as a "city." But over the lifetime of the V.I.A., sleepy Doylestown *has* evolved into a small city, pushed from Philadelphia to the south and from urban areas east across the Delaware River and north in the Lehigh Valley. The "citification" of Doylestown has brought more than population growth and prosperity. Into the quiet, rural neighborhoods have seeped some of the problems and complexities once known only to the inner city. In the '90s, central Bucks County residents have begun to have almost everything big-city dwellers do, from technology and superb personal and corporate services to homelessness, crime and transportation woes. Too many people are living with constant, low-grade anxiety because of the rapid changes—and the things they feel powerless to change: the Central Bucks School District can't build schools fast enough, parking in most towns is a major issue for local governments, kids complain there's nothing to do, "job security" is an antique term with little meaning today, it seems everyone is overweight and underexercised, and countless other concerns.

That environment has surrounded and shaped the development of Doylestown Hospital through the '90s. Hints of its emergence, on the brow of the hill in the late '80s, stirred the women of the hospital

The population of the hospital's service area burgeons.

board to go looking for a leader with vision, both inborn and born of experience, who could see with new eyes Doylestown the community and Doylestown the hospital; someone who could respond knowledgeably and capably to the challenges that a successful hospital must now face.

What did Rich Reif bring to Doylestown? Besides his enthusiasm, a wealth of experience: he's worked in hospitals since he was 19 years old, in very large and complex inner-city organizations as well as more intimate, community-based facilities. He credits his 11 years at Friends' hospitals with teaching him the tenets of contemporary consensus management based on the beliefs and decision-making process of the Religious Society of Friends. He'd been involved with hospital mergers and knew he didn't want to go that route again— not because mergers are evil, but because those he experienced were more a financial or legal strategy than a strategy to meet healthcare needs and increase value to the patient. He'd worked previously for a hospital founded by women and with a board headed by a woman, and, like Jerry Marik, he'd been "the first trained administrator" for a hospital.

He is *not* Jerry Marik. With different backgrounds and management styles, results indicate that Rich Reif is the person for these times, as Jerry Marik proved he was the person for his.

After 30 years with one administrator—the only administrator, really, they had known—it must have been a transition of some proportions for the community, the hospital and the V.I.A. With the legacy of Jerry Marik and previous hospital boards for support, Rich Reif and the still-new hospital organization started their tenure together.

That's 'Rich,' not 'Mr. Reif'

"At one of the first employee meetings to introduce the new CEO," recalls Chris Murphy, a hospital associate since 1988, "Rich began by saying his *father* is 'Mr. Reif,'" establishing a standard of interaction and camaraderie that is a hallmark of this administration.

"From the beginning, Rich has stated his values clearly and helped us focus on what the organization's should be. He often goes back to the same basic question: 'Are we doing the right things for the right reasons?'

"Rich has been able to bring out the talents and gifts in each of us and to encourage a team approach. He would say we knew better than anyone what needed to be done in our departments and how to accomplish it—that the desire to get a job done, and done well, had to come from within. When I commented once on his ability to see our strengths and uniqueness and downplay our weaknesses, he just said, 'Why focus on the negatives? It paralyzes people and no one wins.'

"I've never felt he would ask anything of us that he wouldn't do himself. You'll find him packaging muffins for a night shift 'thank you,' making rounds at 5 a.m., serving food at an associate picnic, bidding on an item at the Hospice Auction, or helping with the Community Care Project—and many times, with his family.

"By his example and words, Rich encourages us to raise our care for our patients and for one another to a higher level than bottom lines and 'doing the bare minimum.' He nurtures an atmosphere in which associates want to do more: donate vacation time or dollars so another associate might

Richard A. Reif   DOYLESTOWN HOSPITAL ARCHIVES

take time off with a terminally ill spouse; expand a small project helping needy families at Christmas into a hospital-wide, year-long event serving more than a thousand people; never forget concepts like 'caring,' 'quality' and 'healing environment' when working on budgets.

"I have been fortunate in my career to work for good organizations and with people for whom I have had much respect, but I have never worked with anyone who has challenged me as much as Rich to be the best I can be, to do what is right for the right motives, to go within and to be proud of my accomplishments."

Hitting the ground running

From the outside, Doylestown Hospital looked like a war zone—or a movie set—with construction on the new wing and the billowy draping and scaffolding where the north wing was being reclad. Inside, the work of the hospital went on with as little interruption as possible. But, if the new president and CEO forgot for a moment the weight of his responsibility for this hospital, he had only to look out any window. Real and symbolic, its magnitude was inescapable.

Some projects Reif now undertook, such as the ongoing construction, were initiated by the board and Marik months or years before, and it remained for the new president to complete them. But renewal was on the horizon as, under his leadership, the hospital community ushered in a new approach that brought significant changes to the business of providing health care.

In December 1989 the hospital began a renewal process called The Uncommon Leader (TUL). It sought to integrate the core values of service, enthusiasm, respect, value and excellence (S.E.R.V.E.) into the fabric of the hospital and into every level of decision-making. These values continue to guide today's hospital and to link its purpose and methods in very tangible ways to the V.I.A.'s original goals to serve

Ruth Schleicher, president of the V.I.A., Rich Reif and Judy Melson, chair of the Hospital Board, at the July 1989 groundbreaking for the new main wing. DOYLESTOWN HOSPITAL ARCHIVES

Hearts and Hands

When the 1991 expansion was nearly complete, the hospital held a gala preview on September 28 to fund the cardiac catheterization lab later established in the new main wing. Those attending the gala received handmade quilt squares, stitched by volunteers from hand-screened fabric, to commemorate the new wing and its centerpiece S.E.R.V.E. quilt. The quilt itself is pieced of squares designed and executed by associates and volunteers as a dramatic, visible demonstration of their commitment to the hospital's core values, inspired by the legacy of its founding mothers.

The S.E.R.V.E. quilt is reproduced on the endpapers.

CORE VALUES

Service—*We give to every patient and his or her loved ones unparalleled service in an environment both responsive and healing; the customer comes first.*

Enthusiasm—*We of the Doylestown Hospital family, remembering that the word "enthusiasm" is derived from the Greek "to be inspired," strive to bring to our jobs the spirit and commitment that first inspired us to work in health care.*

Respect—*We promise to honor the dignity, individuality and rights of every person, and to pay particular attention to patients' rights to privacy, confidentiality and information. We will include concerned loved ones in our circle of care.*

Value — *We offer care, services and technology of the highest quality at the lowest possible cost, remembering our responsibility to the community for appropriate use of its gifts, resources and support.*

Excellence—*We want our customers' experience of Doylestown Hospital to be different because it is the best. We ask for and act on opinions and suggestions so that we may exceed the community's expectations of excellence.*

Capital Fund Drives

Year	Fund	Amount
1974	Hospital Relocation Fund	$1,500,000
1981	Progress In Care/81	$ 850,000
1991	Advance '91	$2,470,271

The Doylestown Health Foundation has conducted fundraising on behalf of Doylestown Hospital since 1990, building successfully on linked concepts of community and stewardship.

"Because the hospital family *is* the community, there are no barriers to fundraising here," according to Linda Plank, vice president of development. "The V.I.A., volunteers, associates, physicians, board members and all their family members are ambassadors, sharing the hospital's story with the rest of the community."

Just as in the early days each dollar raised was recorded and then spent for its intended purpose, principles of conscientious stewardship guide the foundation today as it determines how best to return to the community the funds it receives. Because the foundation spends donated funds carefully and according to the donor's wishes and the community's needs, more donors are inspired to make annual gifts and to include the hospital in their estate plans.

the community. The TUL program also marked a turning point for the organization, a philosophical change that empowered the employees, now called associates, and moved decision-making to the people closest to the patient.

Advance '91, the $2 million capital campaign launched in fall 1988 to finance the new main wing, closed with a final total that surpassed the goal by nearly half a million dollars.

On October 22, 1992, the hospital board of directors adopted a mission statement that would serve as a guide for all associates and the board. The statement was developed under the leadership of Elaine Ewbank, board chair, to reflect the legacy and purpose of the V.I.A. founders as well as the current aims and future direction of the hospital.

The Mission of Doylestown Hospital

...is to provide a responsive healing environment for our patients and their families, and to improve the quality of life for all members of our community.

—*adopted by the Board of Directors of Doylestown Hospital October 22, 1992*

Medical Staff Auxiliary

The wives of the doctors on staff at Doylestown Hospital met informally beginning in 1965 with Elizabeth Willard as chair. By 1968, the group had organized itself as the Doctors' Wives of Doylestown Hospital so it could raise money to support programs at the hospital. Over the years, its special fundraisers have included Hospital Day at Peddler's Village, amusement rides at the Village Fair and the annual spring luncheon and fashion show that is still a feature of the club's activities. It has given more than $96,000 to the hospital since 1969.

The group changed its name to the Medical Staff Auxiliary in 1993.

Branching out

While the preview gala in fall 1991 showed the public the hospital's new main wing, it didn't officially open, with most services functioning, until December 16. The services it brought together marked a significant change in hospital health care, as well. The new wing contained surgical, critical care and emergency services; all outpatient rehabilitation including cardiac rehabilitation and the day hospital, outpatient laboratory, radiology and registration services; a new cardiac catheterization lab; PACU (post-anesthesia care unit) and same-day services (formerly short procedure unit); patient billing; meeting rooms used by the public; hospital administration and the V.I.A.'s own office.

Meanwhile, for years the hospital board had watched other health-care facilities with keen interest—learning, sharing, keeping an eye to

Generous benefactors Kenneth W. and Helen Hartman Gemmill at the preview gala for the new main wing, 1991   DOYLESTOWN HOSPITAL ARCHIVES

the future. On May 5, 1992, after following the fortunes of Pine Run Community, a financially troubled retirement complex just two miles from the hospital campus, the hospital reached an agreement to buy it. The hospital has since breathed new life into Pine Run, invested it with the hospital's mission, and now maintains the complex as part of the hospital family of services.

This seniors' community along Ferry Road in New Britain Township consists of 300 independent-living apartments as well as a 236-bed healthcare center offering intermediate, skilled and personal care/assisted living and an Alzheimer's Program. Extending services into the community is ElderReach, which provides a wide array of services to support older people in their own homes.

A busy year, 1992 also saw construction of a second addition to Children's Village that joined the two buildings together and increased capacity to 210. This expansion allowed Children's Village to open to the community's children, although priority continues to be given to the youngsters of hospital associates.

A young celebrant from Children's Village demonstrates how to enjoy a giant ice cream sundae during the Week of the Young Child, April 1996.

Club milestones

Behind the hospital there has always been the Village Improvement Association—owner and hands-on operator for so many years, and owner still. Through restructuring and then a rededication to the club's pursuits concurrent with the hospital's renewal and reorganization, the V.I.A. weathered a heavy burden of change in the '80s and '90s. By 1994, the women were

Mercy and Justice

"The original seal of Doylestown Hospital was derived from the V.I.A. seal.... Although there is no record of why the V.I.A. chose to put the words 'mercy' and 'justice' on the seal, there are, in their minutes, countless examples of how these women, ordinary citizens, struggled to balance their desire to be merciful, compassionate and giving to all who approached them in need, with their strongly felt obligation to render a fair account of how they spent donated funds. They quickly learned that, when dealing with human beings, though justice compels you to have policies, mercy inspires you to respond from the heart to any needy person."
—from Elizabeth Gavula's audio narrative for the historic display cases in the North Lobby, 1994

Doylestown Hospital
The best of tradition and technology.

A new logo was designed in 1989 to replace the old hospital seal. Although the hospital no longer uses the mercy and justice seal, it perseveres in the struggle to balance "mercy" against "justice" ("person" vs. "policy") in the care of fragile human beings.

ready to celebrate a century of good works, and all of Doylestown was brought into the festivities.

As the most vital and far-reaching of the V.I.A.'s projects, the hospital accepted the honor of kicking off the V.I.A.'s 100th anniversary. On May 3, 1994, Doylestown Hospital dedicated its gift to the V.I.A.: three handsome, memory-filled display cases in the hospital's North Lobby. Their contents illustrate and commemorate the V.I.A.'s greatest achievement—Doylestown Hospital—and the role the V.I.A. has played in the hospital's own history by providing the impetus, setting the standards for balancing mercy and justice, guiding its efforts and keeping the flame lit for this hospital.

Two days later, the whole town took part in a community-wide celebration that included a V.I.A. Parade and Victorian Fair to mark this grand milestone in the life of a lively and dedicated club.

On October 4, Bucks County Judge Kenneth Biehn unveiled the sculpture in the Presidents' Garden off the main lobby during a ceremony that included V.I.A. members in hats and white gloves—true to the standards of dress upheld by the club members for decades! An area where patients, associates and visitors can rest and reflect, the garden's focal point is a bronze sculpture by local artist Virginia Abbott Connor.

New services from a "new" hospital

Federal regulations and the hospital's own reorganization and renewal provided impetus for the V.I.A. to re-examine the purpose of each corporate unit that made up the V.I.A. Health System. The missions were determined, giving the corporations new incentive to act.

In 1993, as part of its commitment to its new mission, the Doylestown Health Foundation conducted a needs assessment that identified 44 unmet health and welfare needs within the community. This knowledge was then used to develop new programs or to make changes in existing services. Among the new programs was the Free Clinic of Doylestown.

In the early '90s, at a time when health care was being indicted as insensitive to the needs of underinsured or uninsured patients, Dr. Daniel A. Nesi, then medical staff president, found he was seeing more patients in his office who were without the means to pay for their health care. Spurred by this realization, he worked with Rich Reif and the medical staff to establish the Free Clinic of Doylestown at—but not *of*—the hospital in October 1994. The clinic, says Dr. Nesi, "provides primary health care and allows patients to be placed with family practitioners and specialists as the needs arise." Characterized by some as a sort of "barrier-free emergency room" originally held one night a week, one goal of clinic organizers was to make it so accessible, so respectful, so welcoming, that neither lack of funds nor embarrassment would get in the way of keeping the community healthy.

"The volunteers are germane to the clinic's success, and include specialists and primary care physicians along with nurses, social workers and

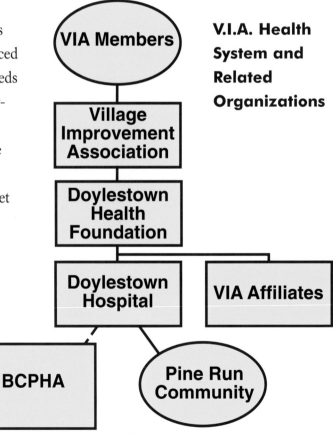

V.I.A. Health System and Related Organizations

Doylestown Health Foundation

The foundation has evolved considerably from its first incarnation in 1986. In October 1993, at the careful urging of Rich Reif and armed with the results of its recent community needs assessment, the organization developed a new vision of its purpose. In simple terms, the foundation's mission is four-fold:

- Go out and learn what the community needs.
- Return with those needs, prioritize them, respond to them.
- Raise money to meet the needs.
- Report to the community how the money was spent and the needs met.

Inspired by its new mission, the foundation initiated projects and programs to improve the community's well-being. Project Fit America exercise equipment, promised to all elementary schools in the Central Bucks School District, has been installed in three so far, thanks to funds from the foundation and local businesses. The Parish Nursing Program reaches out to almost 60 area congregations to support nurses and other health professionals dedicated to keeping congregation members healthy. The Free Clinic of Doylestown receives significant financial support from the foundation, as do many area ambulance squads. Dental Care for the Needy, a collaborative effort with the Central Bucks Chamber of Commerce, provides free emergency dental care to local area residents who cannot pay for this service. The foundation is part of the Central Bucks Healthier Community Team that funds the community teen specialist working to make Central Bucks *the* place to be a teenager by developing good relationships with local businesses and plenty of community-supported activities for young people.

staff," says Dr. Nesi. He acknowledges the "gracious help" given by the hospital and the Doylestown Health Foundation, and predicts that the Free Clinic will eventually move from its current site at the hospital. "The hope is that it will continue to grow until it can assume its own place in the community."

The clinic has also become a point of contact for other community services. Local restaurants rotate the responsibility to provide dinners for the volunteer staff; area grocers and restaurants deliver unsold food to be taken home by the clinic patients; a local organization distributes clothing. In its first 11 months, the Free Clinic tallied 360 visits. The count rose to 831 for 1995–96, to 1,614 for 1996–97 and to 2,051 for 1997–98. It has been an undisputed success.

As the Free Clinic began its successful tenure at the hospital, the

Community Connections: Passing It On

Before Doylestown Hospital existed, health care and the life of the community were connected by the efforts of the visiting nurses employed, overseen and guided by the V.I.A. Early minutes of the Visiting Nurse & Hospital Committee carry mention of gift baskets and holiday relief delivered by the visiting nurse to families she had reason to know were crippled financially by fathers off to war, unemployment, death, desertion or illness. It's heart-warming to find that channel of concern has not only remained open, but has grown to mammoth proportions, involving so many, these decades later.

Hubert Proulx, Doylestown Hospital's executive chef and the reputed "father of the Community Care Project," tells this story of how it got started.

His father died when Bert was just 10. Bert recalls how the holidays were made brighter by the gifts that came from a kind woman; according to his mother, this woman helped the Proulxs because she recalled how *her* family had been assisted at Christmas when *she* was young. After Bert married, when he was working at Cedarbrook Country Club, he found a few families in need through his parish and the local school. He asked a vendor to donate two hams—and received two cases! When he came to Doylestown Hospital, he continued his holiday project on a small scale with the help of Rosalie Mandronico of Chalfont, with whom he'd worked at the country club.

After 1989, Bert's holiday project expanded as an outgrowth of the hospital's organizational renewal; by 1993, there was more money donated than could be spent by Christmas Eve and the project became the year-round Community Care Project. Now an official program of the Community Outreach Committee of the Doylestown Health Foundation board, CCP is no longer wholly dependent on volunteer help. However, staffing is supplemented at holiday time by vast numbers of volunteers from the hospital family—from Doylestown Hospital, Doylestown Health Foundation and Pine Run—and from the community.

Many fundraising projects, including the hospital staff's annual craft fair, create the pot of money used by the foundation to provide food, clothing and other necessities. Bert remains involved, and Rosalie continues to find members of Cedarbrook Country Club who adopt families on a grand scale, helping the project enormously. In 1997, the holiday outreach helped 1,246 men, women and children of the community.

Bert Proulx, the hospital's executive chef, smiles at the giving tree laden with pledges to the Community Care Project, 1996.
DOYLESTOWN HOSPITAL ARCHIVES

168

Maternity Department was completing its conversion to a Birthing Center. On October 15, 1994, its 10 LDRP (labor, delivery, recovery and postpartum) rooms "opened for business," advancing the dramatic shift in childbirth methods from that of physician-directed "operations" to patient-directed, physician-assisted birthing. Mrs. Watson and Mrs. Kerr would have been shocked—as would the physicians of their times!

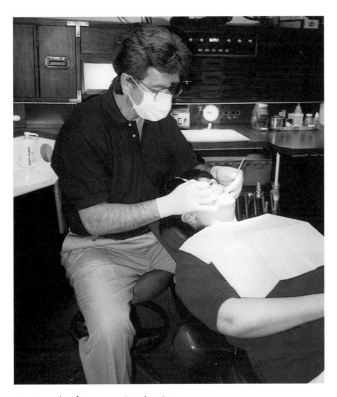

A network of community dentists, funded by the Central Bucks Chamber of Commerce Business Cares program and Doylestown Health Foundation, provides dental care for needy patients. Here, Louis Vida, DDS, examines a patient.

DOYLESTOWN HOSPITAL ARCHIVES

Until 1994 or so, the hospital consistently filled its acute care bed space. But as managed-care companies provided insurance for more and more families and improvements in technology allowed patients to recover faster, lengths of stay began to shorten and the hospital found it had open beds. Closing down an acute care unit was now possible. When feasibility studies showed there was a need for sub-acute care, the hospital converted a med-surg unit and received licensing from the Commonwealth of Pennsylvania for a "long-term care" facility. A year later, the new 18-bed skilled nursing Transitional Care Unit debuted on the fourth floor, providing another option for care.

"We had known for a long time that there was a need to bridge the gap from hospital care to home, particularly with the elderly," explains Mark Pressman, who administers the TCU. "Health care was changing, bringing decreased lengths of stay and an emphasis on care at home. With the process of healing and rehab so much slower with age, to return home after a few days in the hospital may be impossible. That's the niche transitional care fills." The unit offers longer-term as well as transitional care.

Remembering Fritz

Redding H. Rufe, MD, (1901–1996) was respected and loved by his fellow doctors as well as by his patients. He was a warm, wonderful—and contradictory!—mix of humor and intelligence, compassion and clinical astuteness.

Dr. Charles Burmeister (still practicing in 1998): "The first computer in this whole world was in Fritz Rufe's cranium."

In 1959, an unusual chest x-ray in an otherwise healthy, active high-school girl nagged at Fritz. Although an EKG revealed no problems, he urged the family to seek an opinion from a prominent cardiologist in Philadelphia. Tests found a half-dollar-sized hole in the upper cavity of her heart, and that summer 17-year-old Sandra Biggs became one of the first patients to be placed on the newly developed heart-lung machine during open-heart surgery to repair it.

Dr. Frank Boland (still practicing in 1998): "After a few minutes of chatting in the parking lot at the hospital, Fritz said 'I'm standing here talking to you because I can't remember where I parked my car'."

Many years ago, he advised college-aged Bud McKinstry to find a girl, marry her and settle down to his studies, citing his own college experience: Fritz had determined he could save an immense amount of time, which he could then devote to improving his class standing, if he would marry the woman he was seeing instead of dating her. [Fritz and Dorothy had a long and happy life together.]

Edie Hulshouser, early medical records administrator, wrote about working with Dr. Rufe: "His mind progressed much more rapidly than his body. When he had to halt his thought for his body to catch up, he would appear absent-minded. This was not a true picture. He [had] a remarkable memory."

"Fritz Rufe was always telling me to invest in gold," remembers Dr. Donald Souilliard.

Some patients go on to nursing homes, but the goal is for people to regain a level of independence so they can return home to their families—and about 73 percent *do* go home.

Independence through alliance

Despite continuing external pressures to combine resources with other hospitals and healthcare institutions, the hospital has had a clear directive from the V.I.A. since the early '90s that merging is not an option. Doylestown Hospital remains strong financially, a result of the careful management of its fiscal affairs since its beginning. The hospital has, however, judiciously considered and engaged in alliances that allow it to benefit from joint ventures.

Since the late '80s the focus in health care has gradually moved away from what was, in effect, "sick care." Instead of pouring all efforts and resources into acute care after someone becomes ill, doctors and healthcare institutions began to put their energies—and money—into keeping people healthy—truly "health care."

Today, the way health care is provided to this community is greatly impacted by the BCPHA—the Bucks County Physician-Hospital Alliance, created in 1989 between Doylestown Hospital and the Doylestown Independent Practice Association, an alliance of physicians on Doylestown Hospital's staff. As one of the founding PHOs—physician-hospital organizations—that formed PennCARE[SM] in 1996, BCPHA now shares sufficient clout and resources to negotiate with managed-care companies in ways that enable the alliance to actively manage the *health* of patients—rather than merely respond to their illnesses.

It takes fewer resources to care for a well community than an ill one: maintaining health is cheaper than fixing illness or injury. With decisions about a patient's treatment now in the hands of the people

Getting Fit
...the Next Generation

"Did you know that Doyle Elementary was the first school to get Project Fit? That's because the hospital gave money to help build it. And it's really neat. You're having fun, and you don't even know that you're getting stronger! My favorite part is doing 'the ladder' backwards, but it's harder to do it that way."
—*Doyle second-grader*

Amanda Gilmore on Project Fit America at Doyle Elementary School, 1996

DOYLESTOWN HOSPITAL ARCHIVES

The Juniors' Legacy of Care

The Junior Woman's Club adopted pediatrics as its special concern—which was natural for this group of mostly young mothers, meeting at night after husbands could be home with the kids.

"We bought every blanket, every feeding spoon, rocking chairs, cribs, everything—not salaries, but any supplies, any training, new programs, new beds," says Judy Melson, president of the Juniors 1964–65.

Its many fundraising activities—most notably the Village Fair and 12 years of Christmas House Tours—provided well over a half million dollars to support the children's ward and other projects in the hospital and community.

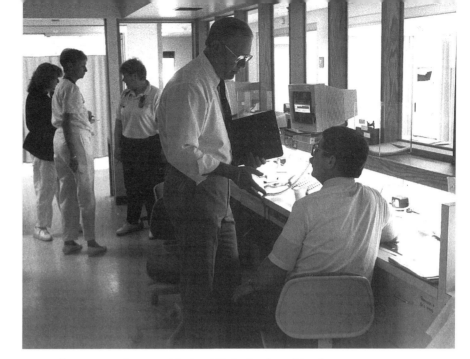

Drs. William R. Barnhurst and Richard H. Rathgeber with other Emergency Department staff

COURTESY: © STEPHEN BARTH

providing that treatment, the hospital and doctors have greater, more local control over medical-management decisions. The community wins because its citizens are encouraged and assisted by the experts in health care to become and stay healthy, and it wins again because its healthcare providers—hospital family and physicians—remain strong, vital threads in the community's fabric.

The paradox, notes Bob Bauer, Doylestown Hospital's CFO and senior vice president/COO of PennCARE, is that PennCARE is composed of systems looking to partner *more* so they can *remain* independent. It's the future—in the present.

In the same spirit, three local hospitals—Doylestown, Grand View in Sellersville and North Penn in Lansdale—joined to form Trinity Health Care Alliance in spring 1997 to coordinate operational services that are more local in nature and to share resources. The Bux-Mont region benefits because these three partners now collaborate on services and eschew competition.

Systems and services

B y 1991, it had become clear to hospital administrators that survivors in the future of health care would be the high-quality, low-cost providers. With this in mind, the hospital launched an initiative to significantly reduce costs without sacrificing quality or laying off any associates. In mid-1996, the goal was met. "But to get there," explains Jim Brownlow, "we changed systems, job duties, pay rates and grades, and went through a controlled reduction in staff using enhanced early retirement and retraining."

And because the pressure is relentless to maintain quality, expand services and keep costs under control, the hospital next instituted a formal systems redesign. Ideas from all associates and from patient

Signs of the Times, 1997
Martha Sine of the hospital's Gift Shop reports that on *one* afternoon in November 1997, between the hours of 1:00 and 4:00, the Gift Shop sold $1,700 worth of Beanie Babies®, a new item on its shelves. When the shop's supply sold out, the beleaguered volunteers had to lock the door. This brief but impressive foray into big business brought in $5,744.64 in just one week.

Women's Health Care

When research in the mid-'80s indicated that local services for women were inadequate for the population, forcing women to go outside their home community for such care, the hospital board felt strongly that, as a hospital founded by women, it had to meet these needs. It helped open a women's diagnostic center at 800 West State Street in December 1988; when it expanded obstetrics in late 1994, the hospital brought in top-rated gynecologist Eileen Engle, MD, to provide leadership in promoting women's health issues.

In June 1997, the Women's Diagnostic Center moved into renovated space in the hospital's main wing, offering enhanced diagnostic testing with new equipment and expanded services. The center's patients can now receive mammography, stereotactic breast biopsy and DEXA bone density studies all in one location. The V.I.A.'s 1996 Bucks County Designer House provided $66,500 toward the purchase of the DEXA machine, which helps diagnose osteoporosis. The Warrington Woman's Club, which has generously supported the hospital for decades, donated funds in 1997 to enhance the center's lending library.

Aerial view, circa 1991

surveys were gathered and examined; "best practices" from other institutions were studied. Re-engineering teams were then able to identify "system fixes." These teams set to work in July 1995 to radically redesign the hospital's systems, completing implementation in early 1998. How the hospital provides care and how people access the system are the most fundamentally redesigned features. Ideas range from partnering with physicians' practices to streamline registration and scheduling, to installing an automated time and attendance program that would, among other benefits, free managers to concentrate on more consequential issues. Patient satisfaction surveys track responses to the

175

changes. The objective continues to be to find the best ways to deliver the highest quality service, focused on the patient and the patient's family, at the best price.

In many ways, Doylestown Hospital's reputation has rested on the value of its volunteers, the earliest of whom were those members of the Visiting Nurse & Hospital Committee of the V.I.A. who did the work themselves or found people who would. They sewed, weeded, painted, canned, shopped, paid bills, raised money, hired and managed staff—even cooked, cleaned and nursed when called upon to do so. They consistently did the best they could—and frequently must have found themselves acknowledging personal accomplishments they'd never envisioned as possible.

Today, volunteers allow the hospital to offer continuous personalized, hands-on care as the hospital gradually changes how it staffs its services and what duties are undertaken by the trained and paid associates. In effect, the volunteers are filling in the gaps—just as they always have—that have been created or widened by the ever-changing dilemma of how to best provide personalized patient care.

Once almost exclusively women, the volunteer force now includes men and women, 14 years old and up. According to Bonnie MacGregor, director of volunteers, 1,296 adults and teens contributed 120,088 hours of service to their community through opportunities in every hospital department in fiscal year 1996–97. These numbers are the envy of area hospitals that struggle to field a fraction of that total. Perhaps other hospitals don't share Doylestown Hospital's foundation of community service or its commitment to provide ways to serve, to match duties to interests and abilities and to recognize the gifts its volunteers bring to the hospital. It is not uncommon for an associate to retire after years on staff—and be back on the floor a week later as

Paid Directors of Volunteers

This leadership position evolved directly from the efforts of the women of the V.I.A. who gave hours of their time to assuring the hospital's success and the level of care it offered. While these names are believed to be accurate, the dates for the '70s, unfortunately, are less certain.

Nancy Perry	1971
Anne Funk	1972
Laura Cowles	1974
Lyle Glassmyer (first full-time director)	1976–11/84
Marcia Miller Telthorster	11/84–9/90
Bonnie MacGregor	9/90–

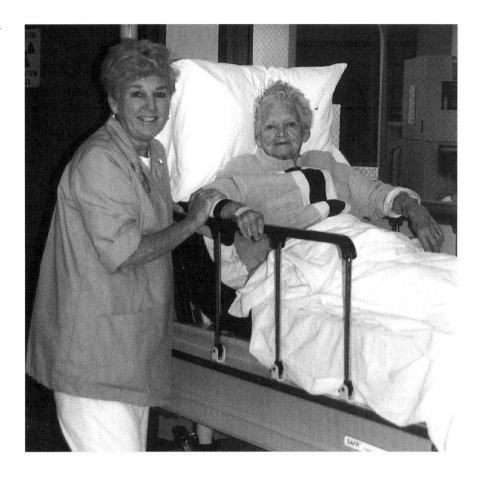

Volunteers perform many important functions, including transporting patients and delivering mail. Here, Jacquie Millevoi accompanies Mrs. Beatrice MacMillan.

DOYLESTOWN HOSPITAL ARCHIVES

a volunteer. Some volunteers began their relationships with the hospital as patients themselves or as supportive family members. Having learned first hand what is meaningful or helpful during a painful interlude or a crisis, they return to share that with others. It is part of the legacy that makes Doylestown Hospital unique.

Helen Molloy and Netta Mason Laudenslager were the first "gray ladies" at Doylestown Hospital in 1942 or 1943. Trained at Abington Memorial Hospital, they did volunteer work there during World War II until, according to Netta Laudenslager, Mrs. Young said, "I don't know why those two girls are going down to Abington, we can use them here." It was Mrs. Young who trained the gray-gowned women to be nurse's aides. As aides, the gray ladies bathed patients, changed dressings, passed out thermometers and fruit juice—did a lot that volunteers are not permitted to do in today's hospital. The "gray ladies" eventually moved on to pinafores, and by the time the hospital moved to West State Street, newly established practical nursing programs began to reduce the need for volunteer nurse's aides.

The original teen volunteers were called Candy Stripers, for the red and white dresses the young women wore while carrying trays, pushing carts or interacting with patients to make their stay more comfortable. Since 1996, Teen Volunteers—young women and *men*—wear marine blue tops, khakis and rubber-soled shoes. The Teen Express Program puts beepers on 14-year-olds, who can then be called from place to place to expedite delivery of items such as patient records, packages and mail, or to assist in some other way. The older teen volunteers can do patient transport and other patient-related tasks.

And just as the women in the '20s and '30s rallied when needed, the hospital still has its "disaster chain," a network that will bring a cavalcade of volunteers to the hospital at a moment's notice to do whatever needs to be done to safeguard the patients and maintain their care and comfort. "The spirit is the same," says MacGregor.

Bringing it 'round to the beginning

With just $1,000 in gifts from the community and an anonymous donor, the V.I.A. brought the first visiting nurse to Doylestown more than 81 years ago. This leap into providing community health care evolved over seven years into the town's first hospital—quality emergency care that allowed patients to stay close to home and family.

New Math

When the hospital purchased all new equipment for its radiology department in 1951, the final bill was $20,000. To fit one general radiology room today with a full unit would cost $250,000. The hospital replaced its shared mobile CAT scanner in 1983 with an in-house $998,000 CT Scanner, providing the technology to keep up with a growing community. Today the scanner alone would be $1.2 million, plus another million dollars to build the room to house it.

Wendy Maven, RN, visiting nurse, helps a patient with medications, 1992.

DOYLESTOWN HOSPITAL ARCHIVES

Latest Addition

On June 11, 1998, the hospital purchased Independence Court on Lower State Road and changed the name to Lakeview at Pine Run. Its 111 assisted-living beds bring the total number of beds in the V.I.A. Health System to 493.

After 75 years of improving and expanding the hospital's acute care services, the focus is slowly but surely returning to keeping patients at home. What the economics of the times has encouraged, technology has enabled: via technological advances and increased training, services that were new to the acute-hospital-care environment just a few years ago can now be delivered in the home under the direction of the Visiting Nurse-Home Care Department (VN-HC). Nurse Munsey and Miz Polly would be amazed.

Today, 50,000 home visits a year is standard for the department—and that has doubled since 1993. The VN-HC's 95 associates include registered nurses, home-health aides, social workers, therapists (occupational, physical and speech), clerical staff and a chaplain who works with Hospice.

179

The VN-HC program hopes to continue the expansion that has marked its last decade, including sharing marketing efforts with ElderReach, with its different but complementary in-home services. Some of the changes that have driven the expansion of home care have themselves been driven by corresponding changes in the insurance industry. For example, as the allowed length of hospital stay has been shortened by insurance companies, patients find themselves back at home "less well," needing the extra help and professional

More Than a Chapel

The Bucks County Christian Council, instrumental in bringing the Rev. Roy Bucher to Doylestown Hospital as its first chaplain, has remained a financial and spiritual partner in the pastoral program. The Rev. Carolyn J. Montgomery, hired when the Rev. Bucher retired in 1985, currently is assisted by eight volunteers, one office assistant, 11 lay chaplains and two volunteer office staff. Pine Run Community now has a chaplain, the Rev. Dr. Roy Lewis.

The hospital's chapel is a quiet sanctuary, its beauty and serenity enhanced by gifts to the hospital to honor or memorialize friends or family. The altar table was made in 1996 by the George Nakashima Studio from cherry wood of an ancient tree that had grown and died in Doylestown. The Nakashima bookcase holds the chapel's resource center. The stained glass "Creation" window wall, illuminated from the outside by natural or street lighting, was designed, installed and given to the hospital in 1976 by Bucks County artisan Edward J. Byrne Jr. of Doylestown.

However, the responsibilities of the chaplaincy go beyond opening the chapel or making bedside visits. Pastoral care within the hospital has evolved in response to ongoing changes in health care, including the decreased emphasis on acute care and greater reliance on home and community services. As health care widens its focus to include those with chronic illnesses, pastoral care must adapt by reorganizing its services to become an essential part of the treatment team and to provide spiritual care to those within the patient's family and full circle of support.

care that the visiting nurses and other home-care providers can give them. In addition, many patients who are homebound can now receive a variety of treatments right there, under the supervision of VN-HC. They need not wait until their need is acute, requiring a trip by ambulance to the emergency room. Keeping patients well is a goal of this service, as it is of the hospital.

Besides the certified Hospice program, which operates under the wing of VN-HC, the department offers home-care services for those with chronic or short-term illnesses, infusion therapy, mental health services, rehabilitation, pediatric care and maternal child health services—which includes the Baby Bracelets postpartum well-baby and new-mother program designed to meet the needs of those with shortened hospital stays. Social workers, in addition to working with the patient, assist family and friends who may care for the patient, helping to keep this circle of support functioning smoothly.

From a single nurse, bicycling through her district to visit new mothers and babies, quarantined children, farm accident victims or older homebound folks, the visiting nurse and home-care program has developed alongside the community and the hospital into a growing body of healthcare practitioners and services. Today the program provides a full continuum of care from its hospital base to an ever-expanding portion of the local population. Through the visiting nurses and the home-care program, Doylestown Hospital takes to the community a breadth of services never envisioned by Jane Watson or Miss Munsey.

But you can bet they'd be pleased.

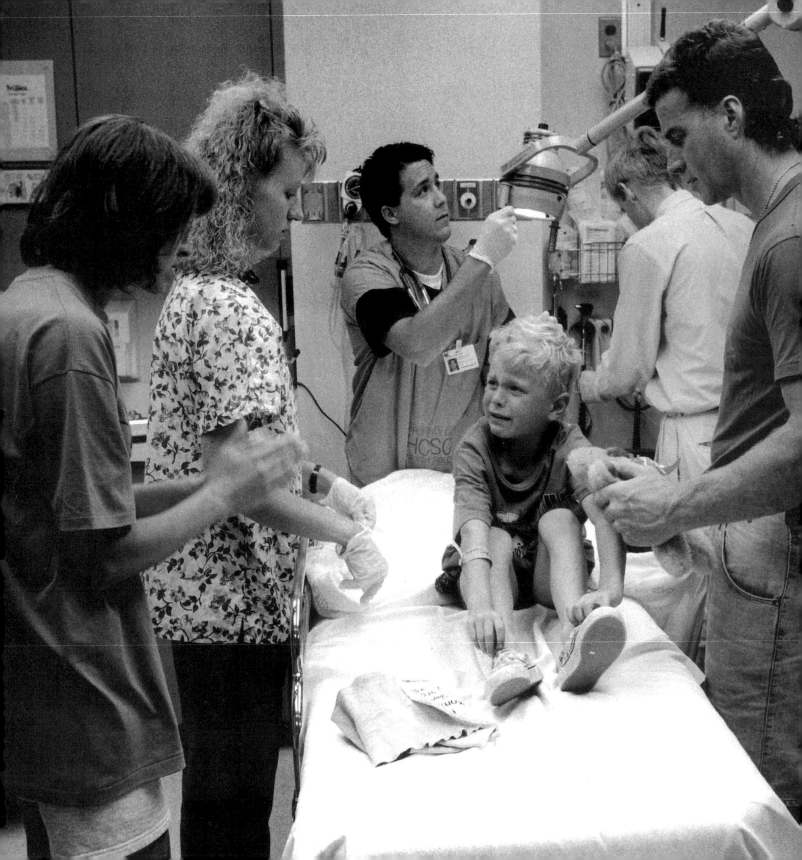

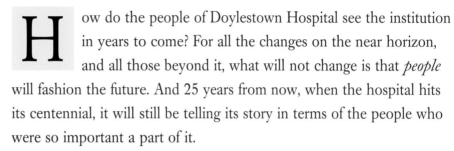

H ow do the people of Doylestown Hospital see the institution in years to come? For all the changes on the near horizon, and all those beyond it, what will not change is that *people* will fashion the future. And 25 years from now, when the hospital hits its centennial, it will still be telling its story in terms of the people who were so important a part of it.

In the view of the men and women who are shaping the present hospital, the hospital of tomorrow will continue to provide *a responsive, healing environment* as it evolves to meet the changing needs of the population. The medical staff—so different from the doctors who literally manned the profession 75 years ago—will collaborate with the patient as never before to achieve the wellness he or she seeks. The associates, whose own label may change as the workforce evolves, will grant a greater customer/co-collaborator status to the patients passing through the hospital's inpatient and outpatient services. Those who administer the corporate functions of the hospital will be artists creatively employing the media of time, money and people to fill the needs of all individuals, identified through increasing interaction with and assessment of the community the hospital serves. The women of the Village Improvement Association will carry on their compassionate and impassioned leadership of the hospital, focusing on providing for the needs of the patient, to keep their community strong and vital. As the hospital moves outside its physical confines and beyond its sterile image, its partnerships with members of the community will increase, encouraging shared participation in order to create, fund and make use of health and wellness programs.

Emergency Department, Evan preparing for sutures

© 1997 EDMUND ECKSTEIN
THIS SELECTION OF EDMUND ECKSTEIN PHOTOS AND CAPTIONS IS TAKEN FROM THE "HEALING IMAGES, HEALING ARTS" EXHIBIT.

Birthday year begins

I ndian summer burnished Bucks County as Doylestown Hospital initiated "Facets of Healing," a year-long, community-wide celebration of its 75th year. On October 9, 1997, Herbert Benson, MD, Mind/Body Institute Associate Professor of Medicine, Harvard University Medical School, and author of *Timeless Healing: The Power & Biology of Belief,* informed and inspired the crowd that filled Central Bucks West High School auditorium. An old-fashioned ice-cream social, reminiscent of the 1920s, welcomed the community's families to an open house held at the hospital on Sunday, October 12. Visitors to the Central County Branch of the Bucks County Free Library in Doylestown were fascinated by a month-long exhibit in the lobby display case that featured physician's implements of the past and memorabilia from the hospital's history.

To continue the celebration, the James A. Michener Art Museum and the hospital jointly produced the Doylestown Hospital 75th Anniversary Exhibit, "Healing Images, Healing Arts," on display February through May, 1998. Commissioned works by award-winning Easton, PA, photographer Edmund Eckstein; two photo-essays by renowned photojournalist W. Eugene Smith; a re-creation of a 1920s-era doctor's office; and a historical survey of diagnostic imagery curated by historian Carol Benenson Perloff highlighted this important collaboration between the hospital and the museum.

A series of lectures on issues in complementary medicine extended the anniversary celebration into the spring. The anniversary year closed with a rededication—the hospital family to its work and the V.I.A. to its efforts in the community—in October 1998.

184

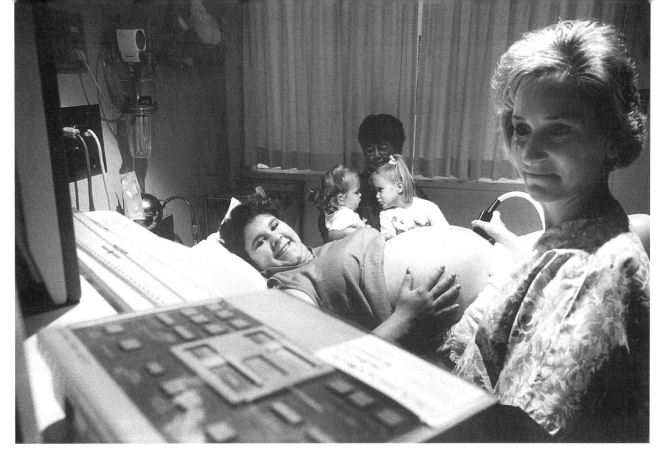

Prenatal Ultrasound Test

Celebrations aside, looking into the future of Doylestown Hospital is still, in some ways, a view back—not "backward," but perhaps a circle, bringing health care into the home again and making it a decision the individual and family are fully involved in.

The changing face of medicine

D r. Ed Knopf sees the younger physicians leading the interest in complementary medicine—and driving the hospital's foray into the subject in this anniversary year. "The surveys coming back from the medical staff, so far, have an overwhelming majority saying 'yes, we're interested; yes, we want to discuss these things with our patients.' I don't see other community hospitals doing those kinds of things.

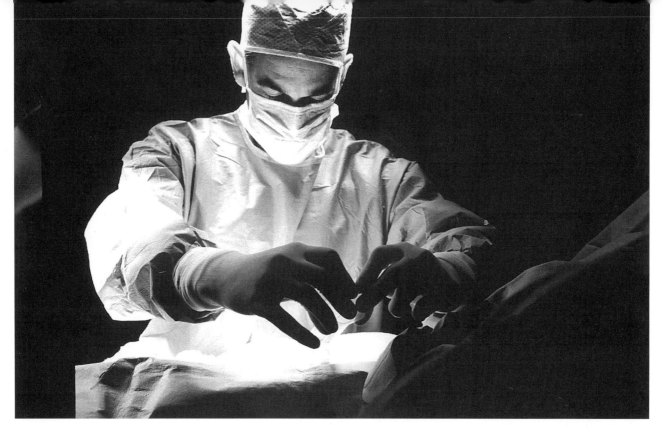

Surgical Procedure
© 1997 EDMUND ECKSTEIN

"I have a lot of confidence that physicians are some of the most intelligent members of our community, both scientifically minded and service-oriented. They don't like quackery, but there's something happening that isn't quackery and isn't traditional medicine.

"The people using alternative medicine are spending $14 billion a year, so the first decision could be the business issue. But second, it could very well be part of that 'wellness equation' we've been looking for.

"We know malnutrition causes disease, but what do we know beyond that? Our ancestors discovered the causes of rickets and scurvy. There probably are other diseases with nutritional causes that we don't fully understand. This whole idea of balance is no hoax, because it wasn't in the past—it cured disease then, and it could very well modulate and even prevent disease now.

186

"The medical schools are just beginning to catch up with this, at the urging of the doctors. Now, half the medical schools in the U.S. have programs in alternative medicine. That's good! And the best ones, like Harvard, are pushing the envelope.

"How medicine is going to change in Doylestown all relates to that. [The people of] Doylestown are very progressive...sophisticated medical customers. They may be hard to *deal* with because they question their treatment intensely, but they're easy to *treat* for that same reason."

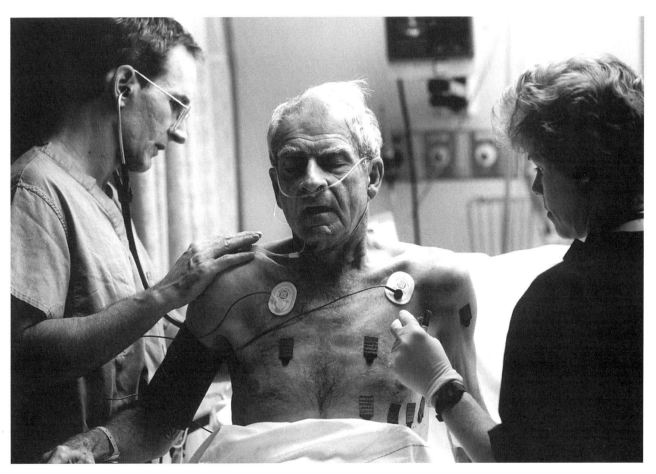

Emergency Department

The changing face of the community's hospital

W hen the women of the V.I.A. are concerned about our status [as a community healthcare facility]," says Rich Reif, president and CEO of Doylestown Hospital, "they worry that the hospital will lose its autonomy. I can assure them that I don't see that in our future. I think health care can be best expressed in local community terms. That's not too different than what they felt in 1895. It doesn't mean you can't have relationships with other organizations, but you don't have to connect them together so you're legally bound.

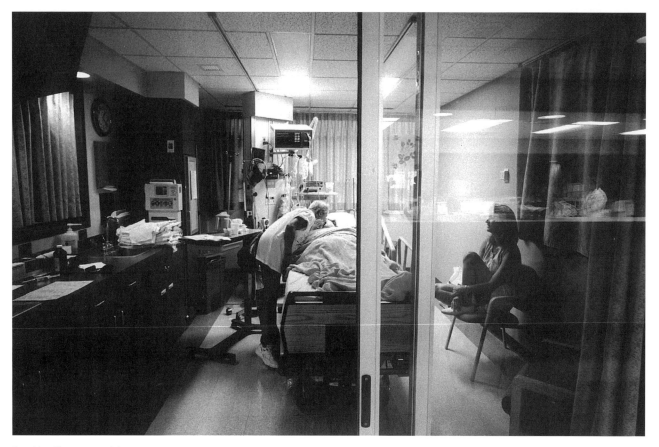

See You Tomorrow, Mom

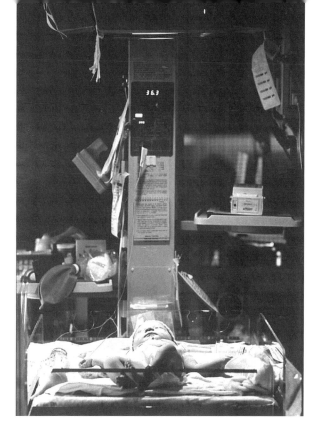

Birthing Center, Neonatal Monitor
© 1997 EDMUND ECKSTEIN

We're by far one of the strongest hospitals in the region, and we're recognized for that.

"When I look at the V.I.A.'s concerns, I see that the philosophy underlying what we do today is identical to what drove the V.I.A. in 1895. We really do try to live what happened in 1895 and carry it through, make sure it's still there. Because of the economic pressures on hospitals and health-care workers, the burden is a little different than we used to carry. That's why our mission statement is so unique. 'A responsive, healing environment'— that's really rather remarkable. That's critical for our society today, and it will become more critical as we begin to look at the issues of creation—through cloning and whatever else—to the other end of the continuum, the futility of keeping people alive in the last moments of their lives.

"Whether we balance those issues from a spiritual base or from a personal context, I think we're going to be able to understand them better."

The changing face of health care

P at Stover, RN, director of patient services, sees patient care continuing to move to more outpatient services and into the community. This will involve the growth in advanced practice nurses—nurse practitioners and clinical specialists—who work in collaboration with the physicians. These roles require master's degree preparation, so advanced education will be a feature of this progression.

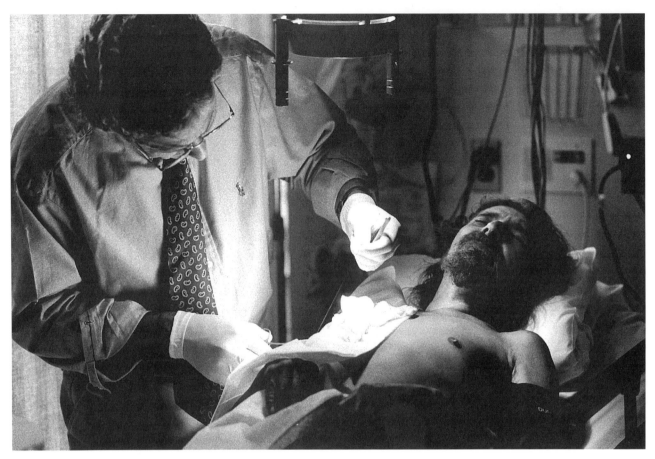

Emergency Department, Suturing Edward

According to Stover, Doylestown Hospital encourages and rewards the efforts the associates make to meet their goals. "This is a really good organization to work for—I wouldn't be here 21 years if it weren't. It supports education, advancement, the things you want to do with your life.

"We have a very visionary leadership here, able to see and move the organization forward. It can see strengths in people. For example, the hospital hired a manager for the operating room who excelled in the crucial leadership and management skills, even though she lacked

OR experience." The hospital was willing to train to fill in around the candidate's critical strengths.

"There's longevity in our nursing team, a lot of loyalty and a sense of community. They've become close-knit, understanding each other."

Does that create a collaboration that translates into quality patient care? "Absolutely! As long as you all have similar goals—and the patient is always the center of that—you'll make the right decision. It gets back to the core values."

Looking at the V.I.A. and Its Health System

When Pat Berry, current chair of the Hospital Board, speaks of her role and the future of the hospital, she rattles off statistics and clinical terms like a medical practitioner, which she is *not*.

"The hospital staff does a great job keeping us non-clinical people informed," she readily admits, which helps her to understand the issues that come before the board and to communicate back to the V.I.A.

"My role is simply to represent the membership of the V.I.A. I'm the link. My job, as I see it, is to continue to meet the health needs of the community and to ensure the survival of Doylestown Hospital as a community hospital under the control of the V.I.A. We don't use the word 'merger'—we don't see a need for it."

Like the members she represents, she is proud that the hospital has "never been in the red. The leadership of the hospital and the V.I.A. are fiscally conservative, very careful about that bottom line."

Her aims for the future are little different than those of Jane Watson, Louisa B. Kerr, or Carrie Shellenberger, given a contemporary voice in the words of the hospital's mission statement. Looking forward, Pat Berry says, "We provide a continuum of care from ob/gyn to geriatrics, we are successful, we are living the mission of the V.I.A."

Full circle, unbroken

I n Doylestown, before there was a hospital, there was health care provided by the handful of area physicians. Soon, through the dedicated efforts of the V.I.A. and the members of the community who supported these efforts, visiting nurses worked with the families and the doctors to care for the sick and to monitor and educate the well. But this was insufficient for a growing community plagued by the need for greater local acute-care services. First rented rooms and eventually a full-service hospital facility filled the burgeoning need.

No longer, however, is the hospital focused on increasing its bed count to correspond to the growth in population that continues to characterize central Bucks County. Today, bed capacity—room for acute care—fails to fully indicate a hospital's strengths. Instead, advances in technology and in the self-awareness of community members, coupled with changes in health-care funding, drive the hospital toward "wellness" rather than the sick or acute care services. And that moves the hospital toward a future as "a hospital without walls," in the forward-looking view of Elizabeth Gavula, vice president for mission effectiveness.

Children's Village

© 1997 EDMUND ECKSTEIN

In the past, " 'hospital' was not a place you looked forward to going," explains Gavula. "You tried to keep out, and we had restricted visiting hours and infection control policies that *said* 'keep out.' "

But for the future, she envisions a hospital that accepts no borders to its "responsive, healing environment." Such an institution would be so completely integrated into the community that the word "hospital" would come to have more in common with "hospitality" than with disease, surgery or pain.

Gavula sees a day "when local students do not know a difference between their turf and ours—when what they learn in science is so integrated with what we have to demonstrate about science that we and they are one community."

She pictures a team of day, evening and night shift nurses, respiratory technicians and other home-care workers assigned to take health care into a housing development or neighborhood—a "team of health-care providers…that 'owns' the care of the neighborhood," changing shifts and bringing in appropriate trained professionals. "The doctor and the advanced practice nurse case manager make rounds—not room to room on a unit hallway, but bedroom to bedroom" down the street.

Even though the hospital must maintain a "few real hospital beds…for the critically ill," a new kind of home care could take the place of many of the services currently conducted behind the hospital's walls. The hospital building then can become a place "of healing…a retreat, a place to come to learn to rebuild relationships…where parents and teens learn better communication skills and couples are counseled and supported through rough times…where the rooms are learning labs for family members who want to participate in [the patient's] care."

The V.I.A. and the community took health care out of the home and into the hospital because that was the right thing to do at the time. For the future, health care appears to be poised to return to the home using the hospital and its home-care staff as the conduit for care and services.

Through it all, the hospital remains true to its mission and the legacy of the V.I.A.'s founding mothers.

To Be Continued…

The Mission of Doylestown Hospital is to provide a responsive healing environment for our patients and their families, and to improve the quality of life for all members of our community.

Touched by an Angel, Pine Run   © 1997 EDMUND ECKSTEIN

Medical Staff Presidents

1954–55	Brad Green, MD	1976–78	Ahmed Mazaheri, MD
1955–58	Redding H. Rufe, MD	1978–80	Stanley L. Goodwin, MD
1958–59	Russell P. Green, MD	1980–81	John J. Choby, MD
1959–60	E. Clifford Laudenslager, MD	1981–83	Joseph F.X. McGarvey Sr., MD
1960–61	Victor J. Fredrickson, MD	1983–85	Francis B. Boland, MD
1961–62	William I. Westcott, MD	1985–87	Edward J. Coverdale III, MD
1962–63	Zachary A. Simpson, MD	1987–89	Joseph J. Curci, MD
1963–64	Samuel B. Willard, MD	1989–91	Robert H. Hale, MD
1964–66	Carl M. Shetzley, MD	1991–93	Francis W. Ford, MD
1966–67	John J. McGraw, MD	1993–95	Daniel A. Nesi, MD
1967–68	A. Thomas Richie, MD	1995–97	James P. Blore Jr., MD
1968–69	Robert G. Bucher, MD	1997–	Andrew E. Krick, MD
1969–70	Charles W. Burmeister, MD		
1970–71	William E. Monteith, MD		
1971–72	Hugh S. Pershing, MD		
1972–74	Richard R. Vanderbeek, MD		
1974–76	David P. Morrison, MD		

Nurse Leadership

Doylestown Hospital relied on these dedicated nurses who, in its early years, frequently provided the day-to-day supervision and minute-by-minute decision-making required by a vital, steadily growing institution. Their titles reflect the evolution of health care and changes in their responsibilities—which, until a paid administrator was hired in 1960, included supervising the entire hospital in cooperation with the V.I.A. women who chaired and served on the Visiting Nurse & Hospital Committee. Unfortunately, the minutes of the committee meetings and other resources remain inconclusive for the years 1923 to as late as 1932: the terms "resident nurse," "head nurse" and "supervising nurse" may be official titles or courtesy descriptions of assigned duties.

1923	Grace Harrington, "resident nurse"
1926–1928	Margaret A. Laubner, "head nurse," "supervising nurse"
1928–1931	Emma P. Stover, "supervising nurse"
1931–1932	Edna Baughman (later Mrs. Harvard Hicks), "supervising nurse"
1932–1939	Grace Bancroft, supervisor of nurses and of Doylestown Emergency Hospital
1939–1944	Margaret Allen, superintendent of Doylestown Emergency Hospital
1944–1945	Bertha Dinkelocker, supervisor
1945–1969	Pauline Young, superintendent, then director of nursing after 1960
1969	M. Anne Cameron, director of nursing
1969–1977	Dorothy Kibbe, director of nursing
1977–1987	Marjorie Franklin, vice president, Nursing
1987–1992	Elizabeth Gavula, vice president, Nursing
1992–1997	Maria Akbari, vice president, Patient Services
1997–	Eleanor Wilson, vice president, Patient Services

Hospital Administrators

1923–1959	Hospital Committee of the V.I.A.
1960–1968	Jaromir Marik, administrator
1969–1970	Bradford Jameson
1970–1989	Jaromir Marik, administrator, then president and chief executive officer after 1986
1989–	Richard A. Reif, president and chief executive officer

Visiting Nurse/Hospital Committee/ Hospital Board Chairs

1916–1921	Miss Jane Watson, chair of Visiting Nurse Committee
1921–1930	Mrs. John P. (Harriet L.) Stilwell, chair of Visiting Nurse Committee, then of Visiting Nurse & Hospital Committee after 1923
1930–1943	Mrs. George W. (Louisa B.) Kerr
1944–1948	Mrs. James M. (Carrie) Shellenberger and Mrs. Charles H. (Cecelia B.) Shive
1948–1956	Mrs. James M. (Carrie) Shellenberger
1956–1966	Mrs. C.A. (Jane) Sienkiewicz
1966–1972	Mrs. Matthew (Prue) Suydam Jr.
1972–1978	Mrs. Julian P. (Nancy) Perry
1978–1982	Mrs. Leroy W. (Vera) Shutt
1982–1986	Mrs. James P. (Betty) Nunemaker
1986–1988	Mrs. Frank H. (Jane) Edgar
1988–1992	Mrs. James P. (Judith) Melson
1992–1996	Mrs. Elaine G. Ewbank
1996–	Mrs. Walter C. (Pat) Berry

Village Improvement Association Presidents

1895–1898	Mrs. Richard (Isabella T.) Watson
1898–1900	Mrs. Alfred (Mary) Paschall
1900–1901	Mrs. Richard Watson
1901–1903	Miss Mary L. DuBois
1903–1922	Mrs. Richard Watson
1922–1925	Mrs. William C. (Katherine G.) Ryan
1925–1927	Mrs. George W. (Louisa B.) Kerr
1927–1930	Mrs. Stace B. McEntee
1930–1933	Mrs. Calvin S. (Mary R.) Boyer
1933–1936	Mrs. Norman W. (Eleanore K.) Lear
1936–1939	Mrs. J. Purdy (Hannah E.) Weiss
1939–1941	Mrs. James M. (Carrie J.) Shellenberger
1941–1944	Miss Helen L. Ryan
1944–1947	Mrs. Isaac J. VanArtsdalen
1947–1950	Mrs. Fred F. (Emily) Martin
1950–1953	Mrs. William F. (Edna) Greenawalt
1953–1956	Mrs. C.A. (Jane) Sienkiewicz
1956–1958	Mrs. Howard Smith
1958–1960	Mrs. Matthew (Prue) Suydam Jr.
1960–1962	Mrs. John H. (Jean Kerr) Elfman
1962–1964	Mrs. Julian P. (Nancy) Perry
1964–1966	Mrs. W. Buzby (Carolyn) Taylor
1966–1968	Mrs. Daniel G. (Hannah) Gross
1968–1970	Mrs. Walter E. (Carolyn) Bachmann
1970–1972	Mrs. R. Robert (Sarah) Dunn
1972–1974	Mrs. Leroy W. (Vera) Shutt
1974–1976	Mrs. James P. (Betty L.) Nunemaker
1976–1978	Mrs. William J. (Virginia) Vandegrift
1978–1980	Mrs. Frank H. (Jane) Edgar
1980–1982	Mrs. Robert H. (Patricia) Yaroschuk
1982–1984	Mrs. John H. (Patricia) Bitzer
1984–1986	Mrs. James P. (Judith) Melson
1986–1988	Mrs. GeorgeAnne Galinski Hutchinson
1988–1990	Mrs. Dean K. (Ruth) Schleicher
1990–1992	Mrs. Walter C. (Pat) Berry
1992–1994	Miss Carel Ann Taylor
1994–1996	Mrs. Ruth K. Boland
1996–1998	Mrs. Dee Ann Woodall
1998–	Marguerite McGarvey

Page references in *italics* refer to photographs.